SOUTH LANCASHIRE

Edited by Allison Dowse

First published in Great Britain in 2003 by
YOUNG WRITERS
Remus House,
Coltsfoot Drive,
Peterborough, PE2 9JX
Telephone (01733) 890066

HB ISBN 1 84460 138 2
SB ISBN 1 84460 139 0

FOREWORD

Young Writers was established in 1991 as a foundation for promoting the reading and writing of poetry amongst children and young adults. Today it continues this quest and proceeds to nurture and guide the writing talents of today's youth.

From this year's competition Young Writers is proud to present a showcase of the best poetic talent from across the UK. Each hand-picked poem has been carefully chosen from over 66,000 'Hullabaloo!' entries to be published in this, our eleventh primary school series.

This year in particular we have been wholeheartedly impressed with the quality of entries received. The thought, effort, imagination and hard work put into each poem impressed us all and once again the task of editing was a difficult but enjoyable experience.

We hope you are as pleased as we are with the final selection and that you and your family will continue to be entertained with *Hullabaloo! South Lancashire* for many years to come.

CONTENTS

St Andrew's CE Primary School, Bolton

Alanah Blackledge	86
Lauren Clague	86
Alice Dunn	87

St Joseph's RC Primary School, Darwen

Hayley White	87
Jade Taylor	88
Jennifer Winkley	88
Daniel Connolly	89
Natalie Peary	89
Alice Keane	90
Robert Wilson	90
Jessica Leliuga	91
Rebecca Lee	91
Andrew Woolner	92
Kirsty Page	93
Lucy Stewart	94
Ben Procter	94
Nathaniel Holmes	95
Robyn Laxton	95
Clare Shaw	96
Jodie Simms	96

St Peter's CE Primary School, Bury

Jordan Booth	97
Andrew Paterson	97
Adam Dawson	98
Stephanie Taylor	98
Melissa Porter	99
Rachael Jones	99
Kayleigh McDougall	100
Jay Thornley	100
Matthew Bell	101
Colette Dickinson	101
Sophie Mansell	102
Lauren Schofield	102
Jordan Bolton	103

Walmsley CE Primary School

The Poems

AFRICA

Africa, Africa, what's going on in Africa?
Everybody seems so sad in Africa,
Where people have flies flying in their eyes.

Africa, Africa, what's going on in Africa?
Everybody seems so sad in Africa,
Where everybody is as skinny as a rake.

Africa, Africa, what's going on in Africa?
Everybody seems so sad in Africa
And when they get food, they don't know what to take.

Africa, Africa, what's going on in Africa?
Everybody seems so sad in Africa.

When I go to Africa I'll do the best I can.

Jodie Leigh Hindle (11)
Adlington Primary School

MY DREAMWORLD

Here I am in my room
But suddenly there's a big *boom!*
There was a hole in the floor
So I ran through the door
I disappeared to some place new
I didn't know what to do
It wasn't dull
It was colourful
No one bad
No one sad
It was always sunny
Everyone was funny in my dreamworld.

Mark Adams (10)
Adlington Primary School

MY IMAGINATION

I can hear the pounding of horses' hooves galloping on
The lush green grass,
Whipping their feet like whiskers
On a big cat's face.

A quilt of colour covers the land,
With buds blooming, flowers burst, blood-red tulips,
A crimson-red sunset,
Yellow daffodils swaying,
In the calm breeze with its cool incense.

In winter,
The land was like a blackboard which . . .
A piece of chalk had rolled over silently at night.

I feel happy now the chilly winds that had a sudden coldness,
Which went splitting through you like a keen bladed knife have gone,
Now it's a blistering sun which is sweltering hot,
In its crimson, ruby, warm, orange, glowing reflection,
Shimmering in the sapphire waters.

Ruth Gratton (10)
Adlington Primary School

LONELINESS

Loneliness is like people walking past me.
When I go home it is like my mum does not notice me.
Children at school kick me around.
After school children throw stones at me.
No one talks to me, it is like I am invisible.
My mum does not make my tea, it is like she cannot see me.
I go to the shop, people look through me as if I'm not there.
I am so lonely and full of despair.

Thomas Duff (11)
Adlington Primary School

BUTTERFLY

Butterfly, butterfly puff out your wings,
Butterfly, butterfly do you wear rings?
Butterfly, butterfly isn't it strange
That your wings never change?
Butterfly, butterfly sucking up pollen,
Fluttering from flower to flower,
Do you ever imagine talking to a butterfly?

Zoe Louise Arrowsmith (11)
Adlington Primary School

WET PLAYTIME

Wet play time, what a pain,
Why can't we play football, it's a game?
Wet play time is so tame,
At wet play time we have a name
And that is what? A pain!

Nicole Duke (10)
Adlington Primary School

THE SCIENCE WEEK

October 8th was how it all started,
An evening of excitement and fun,
Different children from different classes,
There was a lot of work to be done,
Eyes wide with interest,
Developing minds,
Possible scientists of the future, all in one room.

Naomi Bibby (10)
Ashleigh Primary School

SCIENCE FAIR

Bones
Teeth
Babies
Bugs
Some questions got a lot of shrugs

Sound
Cars
Fitness
Light
That's what makes children bright

Safety
Feelings
Healthy eating
Listen to the drum *beating,* beating, beating.

James Walsh (11)
Ashleigh Primary School

ISABEL AND THE SPIDER

Isabel met a hairy, green spider
And on its back it had a lion rider.
The spider was gruesome with gleaming white teeth
And round its neck it had a poisonous wreath.
Isabel, Isabel didn't care,
All she did was stand and stare.
Isabel, Isabel didn't worry,
Isabel didn't scream or scurry.
All she did was cool the heat,
Then she said, 'Now I'll eat!'

Jessica Nightingale (10)
Ashleigh Primary School

THE SCIENCE FAIR

Investigating insects,
Blowing bubbles through a straw,
Virtual babies crying,
That's what I saw.

Assembling skeletons,
Fitting bones into your chest,
Tasting different fruits;
That's what I liked best.

Sound experiments,
More children through the door,
Pulses being taken,
That's what I came for.

Come to the science fair,
There is no doubt,
Learning about science,
That's what it's all about!

Ilyas Deshmukh (11)
Ashleigh Primary School

MY FAMILY POEM

My mum has a big tum,
My dad is very sad,
My brother, Josh, acts like he's posh
My sister, Rachel, is sensational,
My grandma, Dot, acts like a spot,
My grandad, Sid, is like a kid,
My grandma, Mo, plays in the snow
And when I'm older, I wouldn't like to.

Matthew Lomax (8)
Ashleigh Primary School

An A-Z Poem About The Science Fair

A is for amazement as the teachers watch us
B is for the bosses, who were us
C is for the children ranting and raving all around
D is for the drum that was being drummed very hard
E is for the experiments that were there
F is for the foods that were tasted
G is for the graphs that were shown
H is for the happy, smiling faces
I is for the impatient children
J is for jogging to test the pulse rate
K is for the keep fit which made you sweat like mad
L is for looking at your insides
M is for madness all around
N is for the noise that was everywhere
O is for the ointment that you could smell
P is for the pulse rate that was taken
Q is for the queries that we were asked
R is for the road safety that is very important
S is for the skeleton you had to make
T is for the teachers who watched it all happen
U is for the unusual colours in the bubbles on Year 6 table
V is for the virtual baby that sometimes cried
W is for the wonderful week
X is for excellent Intel microscope linked to the computer
Y is for yummy, healthy foods that you could taste
Z is for Year 6 getting paid zilch for working so hard.

Christopher Davies (10)
Ashleigh Primary School

SCIENCE WEEK

A for action for Year 6 to have their Weetabix,
B for baby, that makes me go ballistic,
C for crunch, the stall you munch,
D for down, it's all changed around,
E for exciting and exhausting,
F for frustration, wait and waiting,
G for go and it's just non-stop,
H for hurry, just let me get a rest,
I for irritating, sometimes,
J for Jennings, Mrs, who pinches all the fruit!
K for kaleidoscope that's in our little boxes,
L for looking at the fingerprints on the police stall,
M for moving around the stalls,
N for nutters, don't think we are,
O for oh, you're not supposed to do that!
P for puff, let me have a breath,
Q for queues on all the stalls,
R for roaring, the atmosphere is fantastic,
S for skeleton, the stall that I enjoyed,
T for Tongue, Mrs, for sorting it all out,
U for useless, I don't know what to do!
V for vertical, I thought it was horizontal!
W for watch, the time's gone fast,
X for X-ray, to see your skeleton,
Y for yummy, I liked the fruit,
Z for zoom, all over the place.

Becky Neville (11)
Ashleigh Primary School

THE SHAPE POEM

A
snake
slithering
along,
sliding,
gliding,
it is
witty
and clever,
hissing
a lot,
the snake's
clever-
ness
all
in
his
mind.

Lucy Atherton (9)
Ashleigh Primary School

FERRARI

It speeds through
The city at full speed
100mph, it must slow down soon
How come he's speeding, he'll hurt someone soon
The lights are changing amber to red, hang on, someone
Is chasing him, I'm not surprised, he's going top speed
240mph, it will blow up soon, he has finally lost them, phew
Oh no, he is still speeding, they must be still chasing him in their car.

Kieran McDermott (9)
Ashleigh Primary School

EXCUSES, EXCUSES

'Why are you late again, Antini?'
'My . . . cat got stuck in the sink.'
'You missed the maths test yesterday!'
'An elephant squashed my house.'
'Why were you late for PE again, Antini?'
'A hippopotamus sat on my car.'
'You were late yesterday, why?'
'I went back in time.'
'Why were you late coming in from playtime?'
'I was locked out and had to kick the door down.'
'Why were you late coming in from dinner?'
'I had to wrestle a crocodile just to get in school.'
'Why didn't you come yesterday for the spelling bee?'
'Because I . . . erm . . . got abducted by aliens and saved the world.'
'Why did you miss the maths test yesterday again?'
'Because a python came in my room and I battled it with
                                                my toy soldiers.'

Matthew Toplis (10)
Ashleigh Primary School

GRANDMA AND GRANDAD

My grandma and grandad always say, 'Oh how you've grown!'
But the worst thing of all
Is they always fuss if you miss the bus.
My grandma makes good chips and wriggles her groovy hips.
Grandad likes to watch cricket, to see who hits the wicket.
Grandma has false teeth and she bakes good roast beef.
The best thing of all is we all love each other.

Charlotte Atkinson (9)
Ashleigh Primary School

THERE'S MAYHEM AT ASHLEIGH

Ashleigh science fair was a success
Although Year 6 got in a bit of a stress

There's mayhem at Ashleigh

People doing an exercise
Infants in a skeleton disguise

There's mayhem at Ashleigh

There was music blasting
The teachers only just lasting

There's mayhem at Ashleigh

They were blowing bubbles into the sky
Just to see how far they'd fly

There's mayhem at Ashleigh.

Jack Lomax (11)
Ashleigh Primary School

ISABEL

Isabel met a big, green snake,
Isabel, Isabel said it was a fake.
The big, green snake had long, sharp teeth
And on its head it was wearing a wreath.
The snake said, 'Isabel let's go and play.'
Isabel didn't know what to say.
Isabel, Isabel didn't worry,
Isabel didn't scream or scurry.
She cleaned her nails and brushed her teeth,
Then she ate up the snake and spat out its wreath.

Sophie Waddicor (10)
Ashleigh Primary School

Science Fair

S is for sweat when we did keep fit
C is for children that come to our tables
I is for investigations that we found fun
E is for great experiments that we have done
N is for naughty teachers that pinched the food
C is for computers that are really cool
E is for excitement at the science fair

F is for fun learning about us
A is for apples we guessed as we crunched
I is for dead insects, we had a big bunch
R is for the road safety quiz we found quite hard.
                    Oh, what a fun week it was
                    at our school science fair.

Emily Brown (11)
Ashleigh Primary School

Ashleigh Science Fair

S is for science,
C is for the cool experiments,
I is for introducing the science fair,
E is for eye-catching experiments,
N is for naughty teachers pinching food!
C is for great computer programmes,
E is for excited children.

F is for fantastic stalls,
A is for Ashleigh, that's where it was,
I is for interesting stalls,
R is for running on the keep fit table.

Rachael Alder (10)
Ashleigh Primary School

TROUBLE, TROUBLE

'Why do you have gum in your mouth, Girl?'
'I've got gingivitis, it's prescription gum from the doctor's, Ma'am.'
'Really?'
'Um, yes, Ma'am!'
'Which doctors was it from, Girl?'
'The hospital in Brighton, Ma'am!'
'That's two hours away, Girl!'
'I know, it's tragic isn't it.'
'Very.'
'Why weren't you here last week, Girl?
You haven't sent me a letter yet!'
'You see, Ma'am, I haven't got any paper.'
'Haven't got paper! I gave you some paper yesterday
For the letter you were meant to be giving me today!'
'Yes, Ma'am, but my baby brother ripped it up
And gave it to my dog who ate it!'
'That is disgusting, Girl, it is terrible, *you* are terrible!'
'Sorry, Ma'am.'
'No excuse! So take your gum out then, Girl!'
'Why, Ma'am?'
'Because *I said so!'*
'Sorry, Ma'am, the doctor said I shouldn't listen to you!'
'What!'
'Also my mum said I should never speak to strangers.'
'What's that got to do with it! I am not a *stranger!'*
'My mum says you are, Ma'am!'

Maimuna Memon (10)
Ashleigh Primary School

A BIT TOO FAR

'Why were you late, Jennings?'
'My dad couldn't find his wig so he couldn't drive me to school, Sir.'
'Did he find it?'
'No, Sir.'
'What did he do then?'
'He decided to wear my mum's, Sir'
'And why were you late yesterday then?'
'Dad couldn't find his pants, Sir.'
'What did he do then?'
'He decided to wear my mum's skirt, Sir.'
'Well go and line up for art.'
'Can't, Sir.'
'Why?'
'Forgot my paintbrush, Sir.'
'Why did you forget it?'
'Because my dad was in a rush, Sir.'
'Why was he in a rush, Jennings?'
'Couldn't find his shoes, Sir.'
'So what did he do then?'
'He decided to wear my mum's, Sir.'
'So why did you not get your brush then?'
'Because my dad forced me out of my door, Sir.'
'Who normally puts it in your bag?'
'Dad, Sir.'
'Why did your dad not put it in your bag then?'
'Couldn't find it, Sir.'

Matthew Jennings (10)
Ashleigh Primary School

BAD DAYS

'Why are you late?'
'Car wash, Sir.'
'What happened?'
'Car wash squashed us, Sir.'
'Where were you yesterday?'
'With my mum, Sir.'
'Where were you with your mum?'
'Buying a new house, Sir.'
'Why, Boy?'
'Little sister had a disco and blew up the house, Sir.'
'Where are you moving to?'
'Can't remember, Sir.'
'Why not?'
'It's not built yet, Sir!'
'Well go and sit down, Boy.'

Connaire Hindle (10)
Ashleigh Primary School

ISABEL'S ADVENTURE

Isabel met a hungry bat,
Isabel, Isabel said, 'How's that?'
The bat got ready for a really good time,
The bat said, 'It's my time for crime!'
'Yes, I have a really extraordinary chance!'
Isabel, Isabel asked, 'Can you dance?'
Isabel, Isabel didn't worry,
Isabel didn't scream or scurry.
She went home and came back
And put the hungry bat in the sack.

Desirée McClelland (9)
Ashleigh Primary School

MY CAT AND MY DOG

My cat, my cat
Sleeps in a hat
But the hat
Is on the doormat
So I trip over that
My cat leaps like a bat.

My dog, my dog
Loves to play leapfrog
He has a girlfriend
That lives round the bend
We're not so lucky
'Cause there isn't a puppy
Her name is Meg
And she's got a black leg.

Ryan Fenwick (8)
Ashleigh Primary School

SCIENCE FAIR

Virtual baby is the best,
Keep fit won the test.
Veg and fruit to taste,
The flour on the drum in your face.
Pictures of food and drink,
Followed by fingerprints.
Dead spider and flies,
Lots of children pass by.
Instead of going home,
We measured our bones.
Mr Thompson said, 'Belt up,'
Then it was time to pack up.

Rebecca Huggill (10)
Ashleigh Primary School

MY SISTER

My sister is a Tweenie lover, she'll sit and watch it all day,
She's always jumping out of things,
I just hope she lands on hay.
My sister is a robot that won't stop to recharge,
She's like a windscreen wiper as it's raining hard,
The only thing she eats at Christmas is a Christmas card!

Christopher Rowles (9)
Ashleigh Primary School

MY BROTHER

My brother always wakes me up,
He cries when I go to my friend's,
He always forgets his stuff,
Once he forgot his school bag in our garden,
He likes to play on his PlayStation,
He always follows me wherever I go.

James Hornby (8)
Ashleigh Primary School

MY ANNOYING SISTER

Charlie is annoying,
Annoying as can be,
Takes all my make-up
And then hits me.

Charlie is so naughty,
Gets told off every night,
Really, really naughty,
Never ever right.

Charlie is so cheeky,
To people she doesn't know,
Says, 'Fat pig' and 'Smelly bum,'
She just has to grow.

Jade Greenwood (8)
Ashleigh Primary School

ASHLEIGH SCIENCE FAIR

Ashleigh science fair had experiments that were:
Big and small and large and tall,
Nice and quiet, or sometimes a riot.
Safety being tested and pulse taken while rested.
Virtual baby crying, teddy in a car, dying.
Music blaring, teachers just staring,
Infants roaring with glee, looking at a dead wasp,
At what looks like a TV.
Flour all over the place, sweat running down your face,
Little children getting weighed and Year 6 not even paid!
But first choice of fruit and food made up for their grumpy mood.

Joshua Lomax (11)
Ashleigh Primary School

THE CAT

Headlamp-like eyes shining in the dark,
Moving swiftly, silently, pouncing,
Purring like an engine,
Padding slowly through the garden, hunting for its prey,
Catching the creatures it sees in the dead of night.

Rosie France (9)
Ashleigh Primary School

MY FAMILY

My dad is crazy about ping-pong,
He can't get enough of the stuff.
His beard is full of mouldy food
And he's got tonnes of belly button fluff.

My mum is a funky hairdresser
And loves all the soppy shows.
She believes all the horoscopes
And whatever they say goes!

My sister is into Barbie dolls
And Polly Pockets with wings.
She's all right if you stay away from violin practice
And cover your ears when she sings!

My brother is mad about science
And things that go bump in the night.
He once broke my mirror when he looked
Because of his face, what a sight!

Well, that's most of my family,
Except for Grandpa Pete,
So stay away from my mad house,
On 13 Transylvania Street!

Katy Midgley (10)
Ashleigh Primary School

SCIENCE WEEK

Science week is fab,
Science week is cool,
The science week,
The science week,
Held at our school.

Say thank you to Mrs Tongue,
Say thank you to Class 6
For helping out with . . .
The science week,
The science week,
Held at our school.

Sarah Cowell (10)
Ashleigh Primary School

SCIENCE WEEK

Babies crying,
Skeletons dying,
Fingerprint mystery,
Year 6 history,
Keep your teeth clean,
Keep them nice and healthy,
Keep fit as well as keep safe,
They are all cool,
Yeah!

Keighley Parmar (11)
Ashleigh Primary School

A FAMILY POEM

My cat is as daft as a bat
So he sleeps on a mat
As thick as a brick
He's as long as a pole
As fat as a hat
As funny as a lion.

Michael Calvey (8)
Ashleigh Primary School

MY SIBLINGS

My siblings are annoying,
Especially my brother, Luke,
He makes a noise with his Lego,
When I'm trying to watch television.

My siblings are annoying,
Especially my sister, Rebecca,
She puts her radio on too loud
And sings along as well.

My siblings are annoying,
Especially my sister, Lusanda,
She always makes up tunes
And never ever stops.

My siblings are annoying!

Katie Donnelly (9)
Ashleigh Primary School

ANIMALS

Dogs are sweet
And birds always tweet,
Dolphins are cute,
But not the newt.
Cats miaow,
But not the cow.
Polar bears are cuddly,
Rabbits are snugly.
Hares have fur
And brown bears scare.

My favourite is the guinea pig, what is yours?

Jane O'Rourke (9)
Holy Infant RC Primary School

SSHH! DON'T TELL!

Sshh! Don't tell
Do you promise?
Are you sure?
Can you keep a secret?
Can you keep it quiet?

I know something you don't
What are you going to do?
Are you going to tell everyone?
What are you going to do?
Are you sure you want to know?
I don't think that you do
Because if I let it go
Then the whole world will know

OK then, I will tell you
I don't think you'll find it interesting
I don't think you'll find it brill
But it's cool to have a friend like you!

Amanda Wood (9)
Holy Infant RC Primary School

HULLABALOO

Wind is howling through the trees
Waving about the beautiful leaves
Knocking off branches that have only just grown
Forcing the birds to leave their homes
Whirly, swirly, twirly, swirly
Gradually the wind calms down
But tomorrow is another day
For it to come out and play.

Luke Murray (9)
Holy Infant RC Primary School

A FREAKY FRIEND

A creepy crawler,
An insect mauler.

A stripy savage,
A multi-eyed baggage.

A silk spinner,
A weirdy winner.

A web wizard,
An eight-legged lizard.

A catalogue to make me a . . . spider.

Rachel Riviere (11)
Holy Infant RC Primary School

THERE WAS AN OLD WOMAN FROM IRAQ

There was an old woman from Iraq,
She carried a big, woolly sack,
She filled it with toys,
For all girls and boys
And tied it with rope to her back.

Michael Flatley-Roberts (11)
Holy Infant RC Primary School

MY BOOK, MY FRIEND

My book, my friend
The story captures me like a big monster
I disappear in the page
I'm there, the main character

It's fun, exciting and scary
The last page gets closer
I float back to my real world
The story's over, until my next adventure.

Harriet Killeen (9)
Holy Infant RC Primary School

RED-NOSED

A red-nosed juggler
A rib tickler

A big footer
A silly nutter

A weird walker
A tremendous talker

A catalogue to make me a
Clown.

Adam Frankland (10)
Holy Infant RC Primary School

THERE WAS AN OLD WOMAN FROM STOKE

There was an old woman from Stoke,
Who drank six gallons of Coke,
She turned very brown
And she gave a fierce frown
And then she began to choke.

Natalie Harrop (11)
Holy Infant RC Primary School

DANIEL

Time has moved on and I'm still standing here,
I can't believe I've been without you for half a year.
You left me here all alone, feeling sad and blue,
My life has changed now I'm without you.

No matter, I love you all the same,
We were together through wind, snow and rain.
You were my sun, my guiding star,
Now I wish I was where you are.

Remember the times when we used to fight,
I can't stop thinking about you, I can't sleep at night.
We couldn't go anywhere without you standing out a mile,
With your dazzling blue eyes and your charming smile.

No matter, I love you all the same,
We were together through wind, snow and rain.
You were my sun, my guiding star,
Now I wish I was where you are.

Melissa Green & Rachael Green (9)
Holy Infant RC Primary School

CATS

I like cats they are very furry,
When I hold them, I get hairy.
I once had cats called Bubble and Squeak,
They were lots of fun and lots of trouble,
But now they've gone to another home,
I hope it's a palace or a dome.

Lauren McKee (9)
Holy Infant RC Primary School

ANIMALS

Dinosaurs were very tall,
    But flies are very small.
Birds normally tweet
    And kangaroos have big feet.
Cats sometimes climb trees
    And mice eat cheese.
Spiders have eight legs,
    Giraffes have long necks.
Cheetahs are very fast
    And parrots always chat.

Michael Boyce-Fogg (10)
Holy Infant RC Primary School

THERE WAS AN OLD MAN FROM SPAIN

There was an old man from Spain
Who loved drinking champagne
He always got drunk
And slept on the top bunk
And his wife would always complain.

Sean Stanley (10)
Holy Infant RC Primary School

THE TOE CINQUAIN

Thinking . . .
With slight wriggling
Moving all of the day
Tiptoeing whilst trapped in the shoe
Free me!

Terrill Longworth (11)
Holy Infant RC Primary School

PUSS IN BOOTS

I'm starring in a pantomime, so far it's going fine,
The cast are having so much fun
And I'm having such a great time.
The show is at the theatre church,
So you won't have far to go,
So if you want to come and see me,
Get some tickets for my show.
My poem is coming to an end,
Because I'm very busy,
I have to go in the dressing room,
So they can make my hair very frizzy.

Hayley Walton (9)
Holy Infant RC Primary School

MY TEACHER

My teacher is an alien, I'm sure!
She has eyes in the back of her head,
She can hear a whisper at 50 metres
And leave a delinquent for dead.

Her hair is dishevelled,
Her eyes are blood-red,
They bulge when she's angry
And that I dread.

I'm sorry if my query is out of place,

But is my teacher . . . a creature . . .
From outer space?

Matthew Hayes (11)
Our Lady of Lourdes RC Primary School

Lizzy, Lizzy

Lizzy, Lizzy
    From the west
Lizzy, Lizzy
    Who's the best
Lizzy, Lizzy
    From the mountain peak
Lizzy, Lizzy
    Let's go play hide-'n'-seek
Lizzy, Lizzy
    From the mountain top
Dancing, dancing, never stop

She is lying in her bed
Her cheeks are rosy-red
Lizzy, Lizzy
    From the west.

Patricia Grimes (10)
Our Lady of Lourdes RC Primary School

The Crowd

Walking up the stairs
Crowds cheer frantically and constantly
Player scores
Cheers again, on one side
On other, hearts break
Silence through the stadium
The last second goes
The crowd sighs.

Liam Wheeler (11)
Our Lady of Lourdes RC Primary School

CHILDHOOD NIGHTMARE

I'm a myth, I'm a legend some people say,
I haunt you at night, not by day.

You can say I'm the best at scares,
After all, I'm the one who created nightmares.

You can scream but who will hear?
I am created to reveal your fears.

I give you goosebumps head to toe,
You need the toilet but are too afraid to go.

You put your blanket over your head,
You close your legs tight so you don't wet your bed.

You are shaking out of control,
Wishing Superman could save your soul.

You are hot, sweaty and red,
Wondering why you had to go to bed.

Then you feel dizzy, your eyes are heavy,
This is the part for me to get ready.

You fall asleep, a very deep sleep,
I enter with a softly, sneaky creep.

I enter your room, I control your mind,
I scan your fears to see what I find.

Then you start dreaming, you're running along,
You are so peaceful, you sing a song.

But a giant dark shadow covers the sun,
You find out you're not having much fun.

You are so cold, terror surrounds you,
You stay put, you're stuck on the ground with glue.

You can run but can't hide from me,
The only way is to wake up and see.

So beware when you go to bed tonight,
You might wake up with a terrible fright.

James Haskew (11)
Our Lady of Lourdes RC Primary School

SWEET DREAMS

To walk along a stream of ice cream,
Would simply be a childhood dream,
Where roads are made of sticky jelly,
All kids believed apart from Ellie.

Lollipops for streetlights,
Mars bars for cars,
These lights shine so bright,
It looks such a delight.

To walk along a stream of ice cream,
Would simply be a childhood dream,
With the candy cane trees
And chocolate-covered bees!

There are gingerbread homes
And caramel roads,
Which lead to the field where
The popcorn grows.

From the candy clouds,
She had her doubts,
But it seemed to be true after all,
Sweet dreams!

Bethany Reilly (11)
Our Lady of Lourdes RC Primary School

THE LION AND THE TIGER

There once was a lion
Who had a shaggy mane
And there was a tiger
Who had a good brain.

Who was better?
We do not know.
So they had a race,
'Ready, steady, go.'

The lion was in the lead,
Until the tiger had a plan.
The tiger's not a mouse,
He's a man.

They're coming up to the finishing line,
Who will win?
'Stop, stop, stop the race,
The lion's stood on a pin!'

Francine Stansfield (8)
Our Lady of Lourdes RC Primary School

MY CAT

My fluffy little kitten, Tiny,
Has fur that's lovely and shiny.
He loves to roll around and play,
This sometimes lasts all through the day.
I creep around the house
And wish my kitten would go to sleep.
Purr, purr, purr, is what I hear,
I wish it could last all the year.

John Joseph Vize (11)
Our Lady of Lourdes RC Primary School

SECRETS

It is not fair,
I sit on a chair
And everyone calls me.

I keep my head low,
The day goes slow,
In fear of them hurting me.

I sit on a table,
Reading a fable,
With boys all around me.

They think it is fun,
But I am not dumb,
I am shy and quiet.

Rachel Heyes (11)
Our Lady of Lourdes RC Primary School

NEVER LOOK UNDER . . .

Never look under
The bed at night,
Never look under
Or you'll have a
Big fright!

Never walk round
The bedroom at night,
Never walk round
Or you'll have a
Big fright!

Ashley Wilding (10)
Our Lady of Lourdes RC Primary School

ICE

Ice is shiny, sparkly and skiddy
The kids who play on it, get very giddy
They climb on the wall
And sometimes fall
That's why they call it ice

Ice is slippery and very hard
If they fall through
They will be saved by a guard
They all have fun
Just sat on their bums
That's why they call it ice

Sometimes ice freezes the lakes
And sometimes things fall, they're called snowflakes
Ice is hard and feels like rock
Don't go to the park unless you have a lock
But don't forget that ice is wet
And when you fall, it is your own fault
Because you play on ice.

Aidan Murphy (11)
Our Lady of Lourdes RC Primary School

PLAYING

Playing out is lots of fun
Running and skipping in the sun
On my own, I am sometimes sad
But when friends come round I am glad
Then bedtime comes and I am again sad.

Charlotte Davenport (10)
Our Lady of Lourdes RC Primary School

ICICLES

Icicles
Hanging
Down
From
The
Roof
When
He
Looks
Down
He
Has
A
Big ice
Crown.

Jacques Beeley (8)
Our Lady of Mount Carmel Primary School

AEROPLANES

Day after day
I sit making
Aeroplanes out
Of paper
Sending and
Receiving them
With a little
Message inside.

Stephanie Lord (10)
Our Lady of Mount Carmel Primary School

MOUSE

I have a mouse
And it lives in a house,
In the wall,
That's in the hall.
It is black and white
And it likes to fight,
We ask it if it wants some cheese
And it always says, 'Yes please!'
It lives on its own,
So it's all alone.
It has pointed ears
And white tears.
It has a long tail,
That reminds me of a whale.
It does mint flips
And often slips,
It runs like a horse
Around a course,
It has a double bed,
That's made out of lead.
The kitchen is small,
So he has to crawl,
I have a mouse
And it lives in a house,
In the wall,
That's in the hall.

Sarah Robinson (9)
Our Lady of Mount Carmel Primary School

PLEASE - NO WAR

Why not talk and sort things out?
What is this war all about?
People killed day by day,
All our surroundings soon will pay.

Lots of families left to cry,
No one seems to really know why,
I want this dreadful war to cease,
So all the world will be left in peace.

Nathaniel Yates (11)
Our Lady of Mount Carmel Primary School

THE LONDON EYE

High, high in the sky,
We are on the London Eye.

On the London Eye it's a beautiful sight,
It goes round and round, day and night.

The London Eye, the London Eye,
The best part of London,
The London Eye.

Melissa Seabright (10)
Our Lady of Mount Carmel Primary School

PEACE

Work for peace,
Work for peace, don't be snappy,
Tell the truth,
Just for your youth,
Don't steal,
Just for your meal,
Or at this rate, be kind.

Rebecca McLeavy (11)
Our Lady of Mount Carmel Primary School

A POEM ABOUT LONDON

Down in London, down, down in the streets,
There's a great big wheel, waiting for us to meet.

Up in the wheel, up, up high,
You can see London, far and wide.

Down, down the river where the boats go by,
Up, up in the tower, the ravens cry.

In the Planetarium you look at beautiful stars,
Go to Madam Tussaud's and see the real movie stars.

Buckingham Palace, the home of the Queen,
Walking her Corgis, sometimes can be seen.

The whispering, whispering walls of St Paul's,
The *grandest* cathedral of them all.

Oh! The Houses of Parliament,
Where the MPs sort out the rent.

Then there's Big Ben, Big Ben,
Listen to his chimes when he strikes at 10.

Oh London, oh London, the capital city,
Take a good look around, it's wonderfully pretty . . .

Leigh Walker (10)
Our Lady of Mount Carmel Primary School

SWIMMING POOL

People diving, some are swimming
Children splashing, nearly drowning
Lifeguards saving, Mum's watching
Babies crying, everyone leaving.

Alex Maluk (9)
Our Lady of Mount Carmel Primary School

IN THE WINTER

Shivering, snowy, still snowman,
Cold carrot clipped on him,
Scarf swirled, squeezing him,
Hat held high on his head,
Sticks, stones, to make his face.

Snowy snowflakes, shivering cold,
Floating, flying, flickering down,
Piling piles, placed around,
White, wet, on the ground,
Is a snowflake sinking down.

Cold and chilly am I,
Whistling, whirling, I'm wrapping up warm,
Shivering, oh! it's still so cold,
Freezing, frowning, want to be inside,
Family around the fire to keep us warm.

Yasmin Slattery (8)
Our Lady of Mount Carmel Primary School

MY PET KITTEN AND CAT

I have a kitten and a cat
They play around on a purple mat

They both eat fish, which they think is yummy
That's why they're so chubby and have a big tummy

They run around in the garden all day
Catch birds, climb trees and love to play

Cats may be trouble but they're not to me
They're both part of my family.

Jessica Rowley (9)
Our Lady of Mount Carmel Primary School

AT THE BEACH

People are swimming
Waves are splashing

Birds are flying
Babies are crying

Sun is shining
Children are laughing

Mothers are chatting
Fathers are shouting

Boats are sailing
Lifeguards saving

Sandcastles are building
The beach is crowding

People are standing
Also are sitting

People are leaving
People are staying

Children are running
Babies are bathing

I am sitting
With an ice cream, which is dripping.

Rachel Hall (8)
Our Lady of Mount Carmel Primary School

RACE POEM

I am swimming
I am starting

I am racing
I am winning

People are cheering
I've started losing

Auntie's leaving
Thinks it's boring

I've started winning
My mum is cheering

My brother is smiling
People are splashing

My grandad's laughing
My grandma's clapping

My friend is losing
People start booing

My heart is leaping
My legs are splashing

My arms are aching
My legs are slowing

I am puffing
I am finishing.

Nicholas Ryan (9)
Our Lady of Mount Carmel Primary School

BUTTERFLIES

Butterfly, butterfly,
Flying through the sky,
Flying low and flying high.

Butterfly, butterfly,
As pretty as can be,
You're flying along with your family.

Butterfly, butterfly,
Don't you cry,
Just show the world that you can fly.

Butterfly, butterfly,
You're so beautiful,
Show your wings because they are colourful.

Amie Binmore (9)
Our Lady of Mount Carmel Primary School

FRIENDS

Friends, I have many,
Steven, Simon and little Benny,
Even more friends when I train,
In the mud and pouring rain.

More friends when I'm at school,
Alex, Jake and Laura too.
Then at break time the ground is hard,
As we kick the ball around the yard.

Then at three we say our prayers
And then put up our chairs,
We go outside and guess who's there?
Little Nat with long brown hair.

Aaron Schofield (8)
Our Lady of Mount Carmel Primary School

PETS

Cats have kittens and kittens are cute,
Dogs have puppies and puppies lick you,
Hamsters sleep all day through,
They wake up and eat for two.

Budgies sit upon their perch,
Flutter round and often chirp,
Goldfish swim in their bowl,
Lots of fish become a shoal.

Rabbits like dandelion leaves,
They hop around and hide in trees,
Snakes have skin that's dry and smooth,
They slither round and slowly move.

Pets are fun and bring great joy,
To every girl and every boy,
Mums and dads like them too,
They're put on Earth for me and you.

Jenny Fish (9)
Our Lady of Mount Carmel Primary School

MY RABBIT, ROONEY

My pet rabbit is called Rooney
Sometimes he acts a bit like a loony
Jumping up in the air, without a care
He often leaps from chair to chair
He cuddles up tight, when he's going to sleep
His furry head against my cheek
With his twitching nose, he has a doze
But scatters hairs all over my clothes.

Michelle Cartledge (10)
Our Lady of Mount Carmel Primary School

THE LONDON EYE

The London Eye takes you up in the sky
Soaring like a butterfly
All of London comes into view
From the Tower of London to Waterloo

People came to look quite small
But really they were very tall
It really came to be so great

Especially seeing Traitor's Gate,
I really hope to go again
To see London and all the fame.

Emily Doyle (10)
Our Lady of Mount Carmel Primary School

THE ROLLER COASTER

Excited feeling in my belly
My legs are shaking just like jelly
The car is rumbling down the track
But now there is no turning back
I've got to face that giant hoop
Upside down and loop-the-loop
My hair sticks up as we go round
I can't bear to hear that rumbling sound
At last the end
Just one more drop
Down, down, down and then we'll stop
My stomach's churning up inside
Now I've been on that roller coaster ride.

Louis Thompson (9)
Our Lady of Mount Carmel Primary School

SPACE

It's fun in space
Especially when the spacemen race
They go around and around
As fast as sound

When they crash
It makes a flash
When it flips
It causes an eclipse

All you can see is shooting stars
Going as fast as speeding cars
Around Earth, Uranus and the sun
All they have is fun, fun, fun

They also play golf, football and tennis
Especially when they're in Venice
They are good at cricket and basketball
Although they are not very tall

When they win, they will rub it in
And walk around with a great big grin
When they lose they'll hide their head in shame
Since they don't like losing a game

It's so tragic
That they can't use magic
They can't use lasers, guns, or knives
To shorten spacemen's long, long lives.

Patrick Rae (10)
Our Lady of Mount Carmel Primary School

NURSES

Nurses they inject you
They give you medicine and protect you,
Put you in a bed
So you can rest your head,
You always are aware
Of their tender loving care.
Nurses they help you
They give you medicine and protect you.

Karina Moreton (8)
Our Lady of Mount Carmel Primary School

SECRETS

There is a key to secrets
Right beneath my heart,
I shouldn't really tell them
But I want to play my part,
If my friend told a secret
I wouldn't tell a soul,
'Cause secrets told by others
Shouldn't be told at all.

Michelle Wain (9)
Our Lady of Mount Carmel Primary School

FOOTBALL

Friends are jumping
Goalies are saving
I am falling
I am missing

My friends are tackling
I am scoring
I am winning
I have won.

Jake Langthorne (8)
Our Lady of Mount Carmel Primary School

SNOW IS FALLING

Snow, snow, falling from the sky
It is so beautiful, I want to fly.
Snow is cold as it falls in the morning dawn,
No paddling pools anymore,
Until summer comes again,
In a few weeks more.

Emily Aspin (8)
Our Lady of Mount Carmel Primary School

WHAT IS THE MOON?

The moon is a piece of silver on a dark piece of paper.
The moon is a silver coin tossed up high into the night sky.
The moon is like a drop of white paint on a black shoe.
The moon is a ghost sweeping along in the darkness.
The moon is a ball of cheese spinning around in space.
The moon is a ball reflecting in the sea.

Alessia Prete (10)
Our Lady of Mount Carmel Primary School

DRINKING SHERRY

There once was a man from Bury
Who drank a lot of sherry
He fell down the drain
And shouted for Wayne
Who came along in a hurry.

Danielle Harman (10)
Our Lady of Mount Carmel Primary School

FIRE CINQUAIN

Fire
Crispy, crackling,
Smoky, snapping, sparking,
Red and yellow, orange flames fly.
Fire.

Francesca Shipley-Cole (8)
Our Lady of Mount Carmel Primary School

OUR CAT

Our cat's a terrible bore
He won't use the cat flap anymore
He starts up a fight
For his animal rights
And insists on using the door.

Stacey Vickers (11)
Our Lady of Mount Carmel Primary School

THE TRAVELLER

The traveller leaves on his horse,
But then he hears a sound,
Back in the moonlit house there are ghosts
And they're creeping around.
He turns back, leaving his horse to eat,
Then he went up to the door.
The ghosts all disappeared,
So he knocked even more.
Then suddenly the door swung open,
He didn't want to step inside,
It might be a trap.
So he jumped on his horse ready to ride,
As they galloped off into the darkness,
He heard laughing as he went,
The traveller kept on riding until he rode
All the way to Kent.

Hannah Wrennall (10)
St Andrew's CE Primary School, Bolton

IN THE NIGHT

Sprinting through the cold night air,
Through the forest he went,
The moonlight shone through the gaps in the trees,
In the bushes he smelt a funny scent,
The chilly wind brushed against his head,
He was getting closer to his home,
There it was in front of him,
A little cottage, alone.

Bethany Knight (10)
St Andrew's CE Primary School, Bolton

THE PASSENGER

As he rides away on his galloping horse,
The sound echoes in his head,
The way they speak frightens him,
But the voice was all that was said.
Ay, they come again one last time,
'Who goes there?' he says.
Ay, the wind howls, ay the trees sway,
He watches with not a twitch of the head.
The phantoms listen as he begins to ride again.
The horse chomping the grass,
They begin to gather around him,
But he can just pass.
Deeper and deeper into the forest he goes,
On his horse so fast,
While the phantoms slither away, at least the bad has passed.
His soul lies anonymous, it was never told,
Further into the forest he goes,
But coming his way in the distance, he'll never know.

Megan Davies (11)
St Andrew's CE Primary School, Bolton

THE RAIN

I am as wet as a big deep puddle,
But I can get you in a muddle.
I can be rough and come down fast
And that's why people just walk past.
Don't be nasty, you really need me,
So the plants don't die, they need to drink me.
You need to realise that I'm helping you,
So don't take me for granted and like me too.

Rebecca Lawson (11)
St Andrew's CE Primary School, Bolton

EVACUEE

I hate being evacuated, it makes me feel right sad
I really miss my mum and especially my dad
When I was on the train, leaving behind my house
I felt so small and quiet, quiet as a mouse
The train driver was jolly, a friendly old chap
But I did not feel happy, I'm sure that he knew that
As we slipped onto the platform, I held a picture tight
It was a picture of Mum and Dad who I loved with all my might
We lined up in front of people, who treated us like dirt
One of the women I hated the most was an ugly lady with a skirt
So as everyone got took away, I wished I was at home
With my mum and with my dad, I wished I was at home
So as no one picked me, the office picked up the phone
They rung my mum and rung my dad, I was going home.

Chris Rowlands (10)
St Andrew's CE Primary School, Bolton

THE NIGHT RIDER

He went galloping through the forest,
Eyes watching all around.
The hooves of his horse beneath him,
Plunging into the ground.
The moon shining through the gaps in the branches,
The cold wind blowing against his face.
The trees covered with insects,
He didn't like this place.
His destination was anonymous,
His purpose was unknown.
He was a lonely traveller,
A traveller without a home.

Jake Aspinall (11)
St Andrew's CE Primary School, Bolton

EVACUEE

All alone, sat on the train,
not knowing anyone but Ted, the rest are sat singing,
while I am crying instead.

We line up in a great big hall,
people walk past us, big and tall,
acting like they own us all, they pick us out one by one.

As we get picked, one old lady looks at me,
she picks me up and cuddles me
and says, 'You're coming with me!'

As I write this poem, I see how much they're worth,
I've always taken them for granted
since the day of my birth.

The wonderful old lady cuddled me every night,
she said she knew the fright
in World War One!

Claire Gardiner (10)
St Andrew's CE Primary School, Bolton

THE EARTHQUAKE

I'm an earthquake, I shake tall towers,
I rumble and tumble and kill tiny flowers.

I am deadly and evil and full of life,
I am lurking about waiting to be a deadly knife.

Then I start to jiggle about, is this one coming?
I start to move and people are screaming,
Are they waiting or are they running?

Zoë Moulton (10)
St Andrew's CE Primary School, Bolton

THE TRAVELLER'S JOURNEY

As the traveller leaves, a noise is heard,
From the moonlit house of the listeners' world.
Then the traveller stops on the ferny floor,
He approaches the house and knocks on the door.
'I heard a strange noise,' the traveller said,
'I know you are in there and I shall be led.'
He creaked the door open and wandered inside.
'I promised I would come,' he said 'and you cannot hide.'
His heart hovered him forwards up the dusty stairs,
He crept in different rooms of the quiet listeners' lairs.
One of the rooms he entered beckoned him to come in,
It seemed to be a high turret, unusual and thin.
No one knows to this day what happened to that man,
For the listeners are secretive and never share their plan.
For when the traveller went inside, tired and lame,
He didn't have a clue that he would never come out again . . .

Eve Critchlow (10)
St Andrew's CE Primary School, Bolton

THE LISTENERS (THE TRAVELLER)

In the cold and silent night
The traveller is not in sight
As the listeners creep and stare
No sound is made anywhere
For the traveller it is quite a fright
Nobody answered the door that night
He plodded on with his horse
Into the silent night.

Adam Sharples (11)
St Andrew's CE Primary School, Bolton

EVACUEE

Every night I lie awake,
Hoping I'll stay for mine and my parents' sake.
I pray all day, I pray all night,
My parents hoping I'll stay in sight.
I keep on crying, my parents keep on sighing.

I really would like to stay
And I really don't want to go away.
I'm so sad,
I miss my mum but especially my dad.

I walk down the street,
With shuffling feet,
That's why I hope I'll stay on this street.

Samantha Southern (10)
St Andrew's CE Primary School, Bolton

THE SUN

I am the sun as pretty as can be,
My colours shine out which proves that I'm me.

My reflection shines on the riverbed,
When it goes dark, I can rest my head.

I light up the world with all of my power,
Then I fade at night, hour by hour.

Until it goes dark, I am really steady,
When I am up, I start to get ready.

I am the sun, I can be very quiet,
I am the sun, I never make a riot.

Abigail Tomkinson (11)
St Andrew's CE Primary School, Bolton

MOVING

Tired, scared and confused, the boy looked in his face,
Tears crawled down each cheek as he rolled along the track.
Worried, terrified and lonely, he sat alone in his seat,
Watching his mum disappear in the smoke.
He was afraid but tried to cover it,
Finally the train was far in the distance,
He sat back with a big gulp!

Emma Lillywhite (10)
St Andrew's CE Primary School, Bolton

EVACUEE

E   is for a lonely evacuee,
V   is for very scared.
A   is for afraid, not knowing what's going to happen,
C   is for confused, not knowing where you are.
U   is for useless, just walking around,
E   is for eyes, staring at you.
E   is for a lonely evacuee.

Taylor Fisher (10)
St Andrew's CE Primary School, Bolton

THE SEA

I can splash, crash and bash about
And if I see a boat, I start to shout.
I shout so loud, I jump and wail,
The boat has no chance, it shall break a sail!
I don't know why, but after a while,
I go to sleep and start to smile!

Harley Fraser (10)
St Andrew's CE Primary School, Bolton

THE LISTENERS

Galloping slowly through the forest,
The man could not hear a sound.
No whistle from the trees,
No beating on the ground,
No crunching from the leaves,
Just a silent silver moon.
He stared at the moon with its shining face,
With a shining silver gloom.
The man could see a person.
Not a common thing to see,
For the forest was a dreary place
And the only man was he.
The man said, 'Go on through the forest,
There you will find a house.
Promise me you will go in,
It's as quiet as a mouse.'
He galloped through the forest,
But he felt like being he was being watched.
Then suddenly he saw the house,
So he rushed in and closed the latch.
'Whoever you are, wherever you are,
If you cannot be heard,
Just tell the man that came to me,
That I have kept my word.'
The man did not understand
Why no one was in sight,
So the hoarse man jumped on his horse
And rode gallantly through the night.

Michael Solaymantash (10)
St Andrew's CE Primary School, Bolton

Is Anyone There?

'Is anyone there?' he called as he rode.
'Is anyone there?' he said.
'Is anyone there?' he shouted,
then quickly turned his head.

He had heard the soft padding of feet in the snow,
the soft flutter of birds in flight,
as he turned around, silent, still and sad,
on that moonlit starry night.

'Please come out if you're hiding,' he called.
'Please come out, let us meet,
for I know you are here in the forest,
I've heard your padding feet.

Please come out, let me see you again,
I went to the house, you weren't there.
Do you really not want to see me again?
Do you really not care?'

He rode away that night thinking,
why did they do this to me?
And not to be there inside the house,
when I came to see.

But the listeners were listening no more.

Lauren Stainton (11)
St Andrew's CE Primary School, Bolton

EVACUEE

E ndless weeping our mothers do,
V acancies is where we'll be put,
A ngry, furious, we helplessly feel,
C rying, crying, hiding away,
U nwanted, feeling astray,
E ndless weeping, cry, cry, cry,
E ndless evacuation. Why oh why?

Fiona Donnellan (10)
St Andrew's CE Primary School, Bolton

MY DREAM PET

The ears of a rabbit,
The tail of a dragon,
The eyes are the size of
The wheels on a wagon.

The head of a giraffe,
The nose of a pig,
That would be big!

The legs of a cat,
The wings of a bat,
Would that be fat?

The hooves of a horse,
The body of a hedgehog,
The sound of a barking dog!

This is my dream pet!
He would be silky and wet!
My dream pet!

Katie Finn (9)
St Gregory's Catholic Primary School, Chorley

THE LAND OF SWEETS

I was walking to school one morning,
(With a grumpy sort of soul,)
When all of a sudden, I fell through a large, gaping hole!

I trembled and shook,
(As you do when you're scared,)
It was very surprising,
Just how long it took!

Finally, when I got there,
I saw houses made out of toffee
And would you believe it . . .
A swimming pool of coffee!

As always, when you're having fun,
Time does not go slow,
Soon it's time to go!
Goodbye land of sweets!

Catherine Fowler (8)
St Gregory's Catholic Primary School, Chorley

PUPPIES

Puppies are the best
Puppies are the coolest
Puppies are sweet
Puppies are great

My puppy is sad
Because he has been bad
I like my puppy even so
Look his tail is wagging - oh!

Paige Charnley (9)
St Gregory's Catholic Primary School, Chorley

THE LONELY DRAGON

Tim and Claire went to the fair
On a Saturday morning,
When they got there,
There was an undersea creature
Who asked them why they were here.

They walked through the gates
And met their mates
Called John, Michelle and Leone.
They saw the biggest ride of all,
It was 70 foot high
And the size of half the sky.

The roller coaster covered the fair,
If you went on it
You would be in for a big scare,
Would you dare?

James Riding (9)
St Gregory's Catholic Primary School, Chorley

MY OWN CAT

I have a cat
I have lots of hats
I call her Molly
She is very jolly

She has a lot of clues
She watches the news
I think she is nine
She puts her food in a line.

Rebecca O'Malley (9)
St Gregory's Catholic Primary School, Chorley

MY PIGLET PETS

I have a piglet,
He's very small.
I have a piglet,
He has a ball.

I have a piglet,
She's very tall.
I have a piglet,
She has a lovely shawl.

I have a piglet,
He's very fat.
I have a piglet,
He has a squeaky toy cat.

I have a piglet,
She's very thin.
I have a piglet,
She has a lovely spin.

I have a piglet,
He's very long.
I have a piglet,
He gives off a little pong.

I have a piglet,
She's very short.
I have a piglet,
She has a kind thought.

Rebekah Waddington (9)
St Gregory's Catholic Primary School, Chorley

DRAGON LAND

In a faraway land
Miles away,
There's a place
Where *dragons* live!

Some dragons are fat,
Some dragons are tall.
Some dragons are thin,
Some dragons are small.

Some dragons are hot,
Some dragons are cold.
Some dragons are in the middle,
That's what I've been told.

Some dragons eat people,
Some dragons eat mould.
Some dragons like it hot,
Some dragons like it cold.

Some people don't like dragons,
Some people do.
I certainly don't,
Do you?

Eleanor Vickers (9)
St Gregory's Catholic Primary School, Chorley

PETS

My mum bought a dog and then a snake.
I like my dog and I call him Jake.
My dad bought a rabbit and then a fish.
I like my rabbit and I call him Splish.

David Bennett (8)
St Gregory's Catholic Primary School, Chorley

A FANTASTIC WORLD

This is the land of dragons,
The dragons look quite funny,
But not very yummy,
That was the land of dragons.

This is the land of fun,
Where everyone is silly
And my friend is called Billy,
That was the land of fun.

This is the land of food,
Where the food is gorgeous,
But people's manners are atrocious
And that was the land of food!

Robert Barker (8)
St Gregory's Catholic Primary School, Chorley

MY SECRET FRIEND

I have a secret friend
That no one else can see
No one in the whole wide world
She only plays with me

If I am ever lonely
She comes along to me
And says, 'Cheer up -
Is it something to do with me?'

I like playing with balls
And sometimes she does too
If you're a good friend to me
I will be one too!

Alysia Smith (8)
St Gregory's Catholic Primary School, Chorley

PETS

I have a dog called Buster -
If he ran away, I would be sad,
My dog, Buster, is really bad!

Buster is really rude
Because he plays around in trees,
He is in love with the bees!
Indeed my mum and dad hope he doesn't get fleas.

Amy Hibbert (9)
St Gregory's Catholic Primary School, Chorley

MY FRIEND

I have lots of friends, Ceris, Nicole, Leo, Alyisa,
Jess and Paige. They are very good friends.

I need someone to be my *truest* friend,
Bet you can't guess who it is!

My best, truest friend is . . .
My mum! My best friend.

Natalie Louise Eccleston (9)
St Gregory's Catholic Primary School, Chorley

FANTASY LANDS

I went to a magic land called Hullabaloo!
Nobody has seen Hullabaloo!
Misty-blue rivers and magic yellow brick roads
Are found in Hullabaloo.

There are butterflies and funfairs in Hullabaloo,
But only when I am dreaming, I wish it was true.
Hullabaloo,
It is not true - but it is for me.

Kristie Parker (9)
St Gregory's Catholic Primary School, Chorley

THE UNDERWATER FUNFAIR

My underwater funfair would be for all creatures,
All my friends would be invited to use its features.

On the big wheel, up the roller coaster,
Down we go shouting and screaming like a ghost.

Up and down, scream and shout,
All night, all day!
Coz it's the underwater funfair!

Danielle Cornwell (8)
St Gregory's Catholic Primary School, Chorley

MY DRAGON

My dragon likes to bellow,
He also likes marshmallow.

My dragon has a very big head,
He sleeps in a big warm bed.

My dragon eats lots and lots
And he has red and green spots.

Maddason Kelly (8)
St Gregory's Catholic Primary School, Chorley

THE MAGIC CLOWN

The magic clown is coming to town,
He has a drum, it rests on his tum.
He plays music for my mum,
He likes to sing on his swing,
He likes to watch fish swimming in a dish.
The clown is big, his nose is red,
He has a very, very small head.

Ethan Woodward (8)
St Gregory's Catholic Primary School, Chorley

TEACHER CREATURE

In school you will find if you take care,
Some strange creatures of which to beware.
They may be tall, they may be thin,
They may have whiskers on their chin.

The students dread their coming test,
They pray to God for a little rest.
The creatures teach them day by day,
They don't care because they get their pay.

In class two you'll meet Mr Magoo,
Where all the children hide in the loo.
But when he drops his glasses on the floor,
All the children run out of the door.

In school we get something to eat,
We get potatoes and even meat.
If you leave just one crumb,
You'll go home with a spanked bum.

Uvais Desai (10)
St James' CE Primary School, Chorley

STRANGE TEACHERS

Some teachers have very strange names and some are just weird,
Exactly as I feared.
My teacher eats lots of toast
And she looks quiet strange, just like a ghost.
She hates her man,
But she loves her lamb.
She has a daughter called Pam
And she's got a son called Sam.
She totally loves Pam,
But really hates Sam.
Just watch for your teacher.

Chantelle McDonagh (10)
St James' CE Primary School, Chorley

THE STRANGE RIDE

A tiger, a puma and a jaguar
Went for a ride in a motor car
Up hill and down hill
But they did not get far
As they fought, scratched and bit
Because they could not decide
To go left or right
Through the day and through the night
It would have been easier
But big cats are not so polite.

Charlotte Davis (11)
St James' CE Primary School, Chorley

THE SEA

I can see the splashing fish,
The dolphins that jump and rise.
And swim about the water-whirl,
That swarms up to the skies.

I can see the floating ships,
All made of sticks and string.
I can hear the mermaids cry,
And all the fishes sing.

I can see the seagulls,
Sliding in the wind.
I can hear the water,
As the land is pinned.

I taste the salt upon my tongue,
As sweet as sweet can be.
Is it the world's wonderful part,
Or what else could it be?

It is the sea, the sea!

Arifa Patel (11)
St James' CE Primary School, Chorley

THE MAN FROM JAPAN

There was a man from Japan,
Who cooked his food in a frying pan,
He lived in the middle of nowhere,
Somewhere near a grizzly bear,
He went to the market about 100 miles away,
It took him nearly all day,
When he got there he had a scare,
Because he saw the grizzly bear.

It was big and full of hair,
It made people stop and stare.
He went in the shop to buy a loaf,
But he found some milk so he bought both.
When he came out of the shop,
He shouted out loud, 'Stop! Stop! Stop!'
There was a grizzly bear by the frying pan,
Who ate the man from Japan.

Steven Wilcock (11)
St James' CE Primary School, Chorley

TEACHERS

Teachers, teachers everywhere,
Say, 'Don't chip the tables or swing on your chair.'
Some teachers are loud,
Some teachers are quiet,
Some teachers are always on a diet.

Mr Green has a submarine,
He is getting a new washing machine.
He is strict and he is small,
He has no students, none at all.

Mrs Tobb has quit the job,
She likes to have corn on the cob.
The students hate her, the students go mad,
The students are always really bad.

While summing up, I must say,
Most teachers are happy and quite okay.
It's the kids that drive them round the bend
And so this is how my poem must end!

Daniel Lacey (10)
St James' CE Primary School, Chorley

MY SPOTTY DOG

There was a little dog called Milly,
Who was sometimes rather silly.
She has patches round her eyes,
That are shaped like pies.

She has long legs,
That are whiter than eggs.
She has so many spots,
She has lots and lots.

Her eyes are green,
They have to be seen.
Her teeth are like pins,
They could bite through tins.

She has a fat belly,
That wobbles like a jelly.
She has a waggly tail,
That tells this tale!

Lee Ashton (10)
St James' CE Primary School, Chorley

OLD AND GRUMPY TEACHERS

Some teachers think they're 'it',
Some teachers think they're fit.
Most teachers stink of coffee,
They always drink it with some toffee.

Old and grumpy teachers,
All act like creatures.
Shouting loudly all day,
Always getting their way.

Always wearing ugly shoes,
Always going on a world cruise.
Teachers, teachers everywhere,
Lick their table, lick their chair.

Laurie Graham (9)
St James' CE Primary School, Chorley

ON MY STREET

When I was young, without a care,
Out of my window I would stare,
At the cobbled road awash with stockinged feet,
Of the happy children playing on my street.

Hoopla, skipping, ball in a sock,
William in his cap, Sarah in her frock,
A knock at the door, quick put something on my feet,
I'll soon be happy, playing on my street.

The ice cream van, 'Mum, can I have a penny?'
I queue up excitedly - one of many,
'Oh that's good,' in this swarming heat,
Such happy days playing on my street.

House-proud Mrs Riley at number nine,
Out scrubbing her doorstep, there's almost a shine,
Old Mr Flynn, smoking a pipe in his window seat,
People so happy as I'm playing on my street.

Time flew so quickly when I was a lass,
Now I just sit and think of days gone past,
As I picture those cobbles, my heart skips a beat,
Remembering such happy days playing on my street.

Amy Croft (10)
St James' CE Primary School, Chorley

HUNGRY AND HOMELESS

Life on the street is cold, dark and damp
No fixed address
I'm a lonely old tramp

Trying to find somewhere to rest
I look around to see where's best
A cold, wet doorway is the best I can find
I lay my head and close my eyes

I wake each morning
To the smell of freshly baked pies
I'm so hungry, I could cry
I go in search of my meal for the day
Leftover scraps from everyone's breakfast plates

Each day that passes
I pray to God
In hope that someone listens to what I want

I don't ask for much
A meal and a bed, somewhere to rest my weary head
When that day will come, I don't know
I sit and wait, cold and alone.

Joshua Smith (10)
St James' CE Primary School, Chorley

JESSE AND MY CAT

I have a dog called Jesse,
Who's always getting messy.
In the house, she's always good,
When she's out, she plays in mud.
Good old messy Jesse.

Lu-lu is the name of my cat,
She eats and eats but never gets fat.
She lies by the fire all day long,
My lovely cat can't do anything wrong.

Alicia Baker (10)
St James' CE Primary School, Chorley

MIST

The fog and dismal darkness,
Musty and grey,
It streams around you like water,
The ghost of time goes around you
On its dusty way.
The darkness of the doom,
Goes on its misty flight,
It stays until the darkness comes,
Until it is the night.

Myfanwy Threlfall (11)
St James' CE Primary School, Chorley

FIRE

A fire is a blast of heat,
Burning anything in its way,
Wood is what it does eat,
It can burn through day by day,
But the firefighters keep it at bay,
A fire is a blast of heat.

Tom Drysdale (11)
St James' CE Primary School, Chorley

UNTITLED

A small, graceful, fawn-coloured beast,
With ankles like socks made out of fine delicate snow.

Its short, smooth, silken fur is as soft as snowflakes,
Freshly fallen on the ground.

It's shining eyes like marbles,
Dazzling in the sun.

They gallop gracefully and silently across the African plain,
Moving as carefully and as softly as a ladybird moving on its leaf.

Its food is as green as emeralds,
Its drink is as rich as crystals.

I am a beautiful, elegant creature with horns as long as sticks,
You'll never guess who I am,
Get working on it now!

Ryan Hargreaves (9)
St John's RC Primary School, Bolton

I HAVE A SNOW LEOPARD IN ME

I have a snow leopard in me,
Hunting speedily,
Struggling through the snow,
Quickly moving,

Speeding up,

Suddenly *pouncing*,
Eating proudly.
People hate them.

Michael Dominici (8)
St John's RC Primary School, Bolton

I LOVE RABBITS

Rabbits are lovely creatures,
They have a fluffy tail
And sharp claws.

I love rabbits,
They jump about everywhere
And they are soft
And silky.

I love rabbits,
I like to hold
And stroke them
And take care of them.

Stephanie Cunliffe (9)
St John's RC Primary School, Bolton

TIGER RUN

The tiger's skin is soft and tepid,
With a delicate velvet feel,
This is not just an ordinary animal,
Because its teeth are made like steel!

It runs into Africa,
With its beautiful lands,
He knows it's Africa,
Because the hot African sands.

He has big glowing eyes
And loves the sun,
But when the sun goes in,
He looks rather glum!

Joshua Hargreaves (9)
St John's RC Primary School, Bolton

I HAVE A DRAGON IN ME

I have a dragon in me
It sleeps and snores
It wakens and charges

It kills and rampages
It fiercely flies
It lands swiftly
It breathes ferociously
People want to stab and kill it.

Thomas Canning (8)
St John's RC Primary School, Bolton

HAWK

I have a hawk in me
Flying peacefully
Suddenly catching
And killing
Horribly.

Sam Crook (8)
St John's RC Primary School, Bolton

I HAVE A SNAKE IN ME

I have a snake in me
Sliding sneakily
Suddenly hiding
Quickly slithering

Hunting frantically
Biting constantly
People screaming, running away
If you disturb him you won't know about it.

Andrew Latham (9)
St John's RC Primary School, Bolton

A LION IN ME

I have a lion in me
Running quickly
Loudly roaring
Skilfully dodging
Eating greedily
Lots of people notice him
Proudly walking back
He is proud of his actions.

Ryan Jeffers (8)
St John's RC Primary School, Bolton

I HAVE A MUSTANG IN ME

I have a mustang in me
Running around freely
Heavily galloping
Slowly walking
Trotting cheerfully
People leave her out
But she does not mind.

Olivia Edginton (9)
St John's RC Primary School, Bolton

I HAVE A HORSE IN ME

I have a horse in me
Neighing loudly
Quietly cantering
Slowly walking
Snoring heavily
They are always stroking him
He really doesn't care.

Megan Povall (8)
St John's RC Primary School, Bolton

I HAVE A MONKEY IN ME

I have a monkey in me
It's cheeky and happy
It eats and swings
It giggles and laughs
It's thin and brown
People want to see it swing wildly.

Daniel Johnson (9)
St John's RC Primary School, Bolton

CAT IN ME

I have a cat in me
Walking happily
Quietly staring
Hungrily waiting

Jumping slowly
Everybody stroking him
Everybody knows him
He happily returns to home sweet home.

Kirsten Rogers (9)
St John's RC Primary School, Bolton

I HAVE A DOG IN ME

I have a dog in me
Barking loudly
Quietly running
Slowly walking
Sleeping heavily
They are always cuddling him
He really doesn't care.

Abigail Baycroft (9)
St John's RC Primary School, Bolton

THE LION

I have a lion in me
Quickly pounding,
Skilfully pouncing,
Carefully hunting,
Majestically growling,
People want to roar like it.

Andrew Spillman-Hays (9)
St John's RC Primary School, Bolton

BEWARE! GRIZZLY BEAR

I am a grizzly bear
I am big and strong
I have long brown hair
And I eat insects with my tongue

I live in the woods
Upon a hill
I pinch the tourists' goods
Just for a thrill!

Yosemite is my home
In winter I like to sleep
In summer I like to roam
In spring I catch salmon where the water is deep
And after that I eat and eat
Lots of fish, nuts and meat.

Adam Finlay (9)
St John's RC Primary School, Bolton

I HAVE A SNAKE IN ME

I have a snake in me
Slithering quickly
Sneakily hiding
Suddenly biting
Hunting frantically

Screaming and running
Likes to be alone
If you disturb it
It will bite its poisonous bite.

Joshua Charleston (8)
St John's RC Primary School, Bolton

ROBBIE, MY GOLDFISH

My goldfish called Robbie swims around in his tank
He swims lonely in his tank sucking on the stones
When I come home from school he hides behind the lighthouse

At night he floats up and down, blowing bubbles
And banging his head on the lid.

Robert Summerton (8)
St John's RC Primary School, Bolton

MR RILEY (MY TEACHER)

Mr Riley isn't stressy,
He sometimes lets us get the classroom messy.
Mr Riley isn't tight,
But he sometimes gives me a fright.
Mr Riley sometimes goes crazy,
When people are lazy.
So overall in this debate,
Mr Riley is great.

Jason Treadwell (9)
St Joseph's Catholic Primary School, Withnell

WIND

Wind is fast,
Wind is slow,
Wind is always on the go.
It blows and blows
And tickles your toes
And it knows you're getting cold.

Steven Rutter (9)
St Joseph's Catholic Primary School, Withnell

THEME PARK WORLD

I wish the world was a theme park
With carousels whirling round,
Ferris wheels touching the sky up high
And water slides splashing around.

Roller coasters shooting around
Coming down, nearly touching the ground,
Ghost trains scaring people out of their chair,
With vampires lurking about.

I wish the world was a theme park
With carousels whirling round,
Ferris wheels touching the sky up high
And water slides splashing around.

Sometimes there are circuses making you laugh,
Jugglers, magicians and all of that,
Maybe a monorail whizzing near,
Not at all to give you a fear.

I wish the world was a theme park
With carousels whirling round,
Ferris wheels touching the sky up high
And water slides splashing around.

Launched Freefalls shooting up in the air
Go-karts driving down the track there,
Rowing boats are more a gentle type,
Mini-golf is a bit like that.

I wish the world was a theme park,
The log flume spreads water near,
The sound of dodgems crashing together,
Is like a big *bang* or a *crash!*

I wish the world was a theme park . . .
Sadly, it's not.

Nicholas Smith (9)
St Joseph's Catholic Primary School, Withnell

WALKING

The road is long and wide
And my feet are my only guide,
Being careful with every stride.

Walking all day long,
My feet are beginning to throb,
But nothing will stop me from walking where I belong.

Peter Holmes (10)
St Joseph's Catholic Primary School, Withnell

THERE WAS A BOY CALLED DALE

There was a boy from Rochdale,
Who looked very pale,
His name was Dale,
He got sent to jail
Because he drank too much ale.

Robert Sanderson (11)
St Joseph's Catholic Primary School, Withnell

I WOULD LOVE TO BE AN ARTIST

I would love to be an artist
With my narrow brush,
Swirling through the paint,
Making lovely pictures.

Pictures from my eyes,
Pictures from my thoughts,
Pictures of all kinds,
Pictures of all sorts.

When my brush would touch the paper,
I wouldn't be able to let go.
I love art so much, even
Ask my friends, they know!

Lauren Kenyon (11)
St Joseph's Catholic Primary School, Withnell

VALENTINE'S DAY

Yes! Today is Valentine's,
I leap and shout for joy.
Chocolate shaped like little hearts
And a tiny cherub toy.

Cupid shoot your arrow, please!
For me and my boyfriend.
Standing together arm in arm
Until the happy end.

Yesterday was Valentine's,
I've had my special day,
My boyfriend has just said the word,
We're wed this time in May.

Elizabeth Undrell (8)
St Joseph's Catholic Primary School, Withnell

PORKY PIG

Porky Pig is so shy,
He is even scared of a fly.
If you flick his ear,
He will be scared to know you are so near.
When Porky Pig gets sent to bed,
He always goes bright red.
Porky Pig is different to the other pigs,
Because he always wears a wig.
The other pigs have lots of fun,
But poor old Porky Pig is always glum.
Porky Pig hates the way he looks,
But he loves to read books.
Porky Pig loves his lunch,
But he doesn't like to punch.
And that's the end of poor old Porky Pig.

Rebecca Kealey (10)
St Joseph's Catholic Primary School, Withnell

THE QUESTION

Why do people cry?
Why does the world mosey by?

Why does the sun shine bright?
Why does the moon come out at night?

Why do planets go round the sun?
Why do people have fun?

Maybe we will never know these things,
We will just have to see what the future brings.

Rebecca Steed (10)
St Joseph's Catholic Primary School, Withnell

THE BRIGHT, SHINY MOON

One night I turned off my light
And out of the window was something so bright,
I think that was the bright, shiny moon.
I wonder why it stays up so soon
And then I told my mum and dad,
When I did I was very mad.
So then I went upstairs to say to the moon,
'Can you go to bed very soon?'

Hannah Winstanley (9)
St Joseph's Catholic Primary School, Withnell

I'M CLIMBING A MOUNTAIN

I'm climbing a mountain,
It's cold, high and bright.
I'm climbing a mountain,
It's a pretty scary sight.
I'm climbing a mountain,
It's such a thing to do.
I'm climbing a mountain,
So why don't you come too?

Robert Smith (9)
St Joseph's Catholic Primary School, Withnell

I WISH I COULD BE A POP STAR

I wish I could be a pop star
I'd sing all day long
Dress up in sparkly dresses
And listen to my favourite songs

I'd meet all famous pop stars
Especially Gareth Gates
Of course he is the best
As I talk about him to my mates!

Rachael Nash (11)
St Joseph's Catholic Primary School, Withnell

WIGAN PIER

I love Wigan pier,
Whenever we go there I always cheer.

My favourite part is the coal mine,
It's so good we have to stay in line.

The classroom is good
And I'd stay there all day if I could.

I really love Wigan pier.

Rebecca Shorrock (8)
St Joseph's Catholic Primary School, Withnell

MY FAVOURITE FOOD

My favourite food is chips, burgers and beans.
When I eat my beans, I trump off my jeans.
I break all my brother's things,
My favourite thing is to bounce on the trampoline
While eating my chips, burgers and beans.

Oliver Turner (8)
St Joseph's Catholic Primary School, Withnell

BECAUSE MY TEACHER SAID SO

I'm writing a poem for my homework
Because my teacher said so.
It's not going to be easy to do,
Because my teacher said so.
He didn't give us any clue,
Because my teacher said so.
It was the hardest thing I had to do,
Because my teacher said so.
I thought and I thought what I would do
Because my teacher said so.
That's why I wrote this little poem,
Because my teacher
Said so!

Alanah Blackledge (9)
St Joseph's Catholic Primary School, Withnell

JESS

Jess is the best,
Better than all the rest.
She wears a pretty pink dress.

Jess is a pest,
She never gives it a rest.

Jess loves ponies,
She also likes roses.

Now you know Jess,
Just remember, she is the best!

Lauren Clague (11)
St Joseph's Catholic Primary School, Withnell

MY FRIEND LIZ

I like Liz
when she gets in a tiz.
Liz likes fizzy pop
and I do too.

Liz is very kind
and she uses her mind.
Liz is very fun
and Liz loves a sticky toffee bun.
Mmmm, yummy!

Alice Dunn (9)
St Joseph's Catholic Primary School, Withnell

MY TEDDY

My teddy is soft and cuddly,
But suddenly,
One day I lost her,
But I found her.

My teddy is cream and brown,
But my teddy doesn't wear a crown.
She sits on my bed all day
And her birthday is in May.

My teddy is cute
And she can whistle like a flute,
She is very small
And she sits near my bed pole.

Hayley White (9)
St Joseph's RC Primary School, Darwen

THE LAND FROM FAR AWAY

After counting a hundred sheep,
I'll finally doze off to sleep.
Once my eyes are closed,
I open the doors,
To a land where no one else can go!
There I'll stay,
All night and all day,
Watching the sunflowers grow
And I'll sleep and I'll creep,
Exploring my world,
Where nobody else can go!
I'll get a warning,
When it is morning
And I have to leave my dream,
I climb on a boat
And sail through my thoughts,
Back to the real world,
Where there is fighting and war,
A world that's no more,
My land from far away.

Jade Taylor (11)
St Joseph's RC Primary School, Darwen

HOPE

Hope looks like an angel from Heaven
Hope tastes like sweets and candy
Hope smells like flowers and fresh air
Hope brings good luck to everyone
Hope brings a smile to every face
Hope lives in the centre of a heart.

Jennifer Winkley (10)
St Joseph's RC Primary School, Darwen

BLUE MONDAY

On Monday I feel useless, just like . . .

A book with no pages
A door with no handle
A classroom with no people
A person with no head
A bird with no wings
A dictionary with no words
A football team with no football ground
A person with no eyes
A car with no radio
A bus with no seats
A river with no water
A spider with no legs
A telephone with no buttons
A bike with no wheels
A wall with no bricks
A book with no title.

Daniel Connolly (11)
St Joseph's RC Primary School, Darwen

TEDDY BEAR

I love to play with my teddy bear
It's soft and cuddly
It sits all day on my shelf
Teddy bear goes everywhere
Its bowtie is bright red
It's golden-brown with pink cheeks
My fingers feel its fur
My cute teddy bear.

Natalie Peary (10)
St Joseph's RC Primary School, Darwen

THE SHOP

I always go to the shop
And buy a lollipop
And when they were all gone
The sun never shone

When I get a sweet
I always seem to greet
The person in the shop
Who uses a big mop

I sometimes get a bag
And never seem to nag
When I go home then
I see my friend, Ben

When I get a mint
There sometimes is a dint
I go to the till and say,
'I'll come another day.'

Alice Keane (10)
St Joseph's RC Primary School, Darwen

BEYBLADES

Watch Beyblades as they spin,
Come on! Come on! Yes we win.
You wind them up and let them go,
Some go fast and some go slow.
Round and round as they move,
Come on Dranzer, smash him smooth.
Now his Beyblade is like chess,
Putting it back together, he made a big mess.

Robert Wilson (9)
St Joseph's RC Primary School, Darwen

MY BUNNY

My bunny is very funny,
He is a cute bunny.
He makes me laugh, he makes me cry,
He makes me laugh until I die.

He jumps up and down and left and right,
He only plays out in the light.
He used to bite but now he doesn't.
He bites my mum but she says he shouldn't.
Now it's winter, he's not allowed out,
Even though he likes playing out and about,
We all love him very much.
But I think I love him more than my brother,
Just a touch.

Jessica Leliuga (9)
St Joseph's RC Primary School, Darwen

WHO? WHY?

I know a young girl with no name,
'Stop asking!' she says, 'You're a pain.'
We ask her why?
She doesn't reply.
'Do you have a mum or a dad,
Or were they naughty and bad?
We're trying to choose one for you,
What about the lovely name, Lu-Lu?
Why can't you dance or sing?
Can you do anything?
Try to join and play this game!'
The young girl with no name!

Rebecca Lee (10)
St Joseph's RC Primary School, Darwen

I'VE GOT FEELINGS

I've got feelings in my nose,
I'm in trouble if it grows.
I've got feelings in my toes,
With all the sweat that flows.

I've got feelings in my cheeks,
That will last for several weeks.
I've got feelings in my ears,
That help me to drink beers.

I've got feelings on my chin,
That I found in a bin.
I've got feelings in my legs,
That I hang on clothes pegs.

I've got feelings on my face,
'Cause I want to go to space.
I've got feelings in my belly,
That makes me feel like jelly.

I've got feelings in my brain,
That makes me feel insane.
I've got feelings in my heart,
That make me look so smart.

I've got feelings in my bones,
That will make me as strong as stones.
I've got feelings in my mouth,
My food has just gone south.

I've got feelings on my lips,
That tastes just like fish and chips.
I've got feelings for my friends,
That I found in a Mercedes-Benz.

Andrew Woolner (10)
St Joseph's RC Primary School, Darwen

TODAY'S BLUE MONDAY

A netball is not bouncy
A football is popped
A mouse that doesn't squeak
A lion that doesn't roar
A wrestler that can't wrestle
A school without any teachers
A life without any friends
A baby that doesn't cry
A street without any cars
A park without any swings
A dad that doesn't care for you
A computer without a mouse
A house without a roof
A teacher that can't teach
A piano that can't play music
A rubber that can't rub out
A phone without any ring tone
A friend that was a bully
A best friend that didn't like you
A person without a face
A life without any colour
A school without any friends in
A teacher that was horrible
A clown that wasn't funny
A circus without a clown
A book without any pages
A teddy bear without fur
A girl without hair
A town without any people
A school without any children in.

Kirsty Page (10)
St Joseph's RC Primary School, Darwen

BLUE MONDAY

On Monday I felt useless, just like:
A night with no moon
A rhyme with no tune
A clock with no hands
A world with no land
A dog with no bark
A day that's just dark
A pub with no beer
A cry with no tear
A pen with no ink
An eye with no blink.

Lucy Stewart (10)
St Joseph's RC Primary School, Darwen

BLUE MONDAY

On Mondays I feel useless, like:
A light with no bulb
A door with no handle
Stairs with no steps
A statue with no head
A world map with no islands
A board with no chalk
A clock with no numbers
A tree with no leaves
A book with no pages.

Ben Procter (10)
St Joseph's RC Primary School, Darwen

THE MOON IS . . .

The moon is a coconut
Rolling through the air.

The moon is a tennis ball
Being smashed through the sky.

The moon is a shiny marble
Rolling through the sky.

The moon is a football
Being shot into the night.

The moon is a banana
Floating in the night.

Nathaniel Holmes (11)
St Joseph's RC Primary School, Darwen

VALENTINE

I believe that God above created you
For me to love
He picked you out from the rest
Because he knew
I love you best

I had a heart so warm and true
But now it's gone from me to you
Take care of it as I have done
For now you have two
And I have none.

Robyn Laxton (10)
St Joseph's RC Primary School, Darwen

I LOVE TO PLAY

I love to play, I do it every day
Football, netball, I love them all
I love to run and have some fun
On a summer's day
Now do you realise, why I love to play?

I love to play, I do it all day by day
From playing on my bike
And having a cool hike
I love hide-and-seek
It's really cool, having to go peek
That's why I love to play.

Clare Shaw (10)
St Joseph's RC Primary School, Darwen

THE RAINBOW

Red, yellow, pink and green
Orange, blue plus aubergine
The colours that bring us such delight
When we have a rainbow in our sight

It brings joy
To every girl and boy
The colours are so happy and gay
And they never really fade away.

Jodie Simms (10)
St Joseph's RC Primary School, Darwen

THE SEA

The sea is beautiful at sunset.
The sea goes orange.
People pack up.
The waves go calm.
The sun goes down.
The sea goes to sleep.
The dolphins jump.
The moon comes up.
The dolphins sing to the moon and the stars.
The stars shine bright, so does the moon too.
The sun comes up.
The moon goes down.
People go into the sea.
The sea animals are happy,
So am I.

Jordan Booth (9)
St Peter's CE Primary School, Bury

SHADOW

It follows me all the time,
Is it an alien?
Is it a person?
Is it an animal?
Is it a bird?
Is it a tiger?
Is it a creature?
Is it a fly?
Is it an ant?
No, it's my shadow!

Andrew Paterson (10)
St Peter's CE Primary School, Bury

MANCHESTER UNITED

Manchester United entering the tunnel
Rudi and Scholes preparing for kick-off
The whistle blows, the game begins
Sir Alex Ferguson shouting, 'Come on lads!'
Beckham running up the wing
Great ball through to Rudi, the king
Kirkland out to save the day
Rudi with an angry face
The first half blows
Liverpool and United tied
Sir Alex Ferguson having team talk
Then United came back on
Scholes crosses, hits Rio's shoe
And puts the net through
The crowd screaming, jumping up and down
United's crowd whistling for the whistle
Gerrard picking his toes, the whistle blows
1-0.

Adam Dawson (10)
St Peter's CE Primary School, Bury

MY SPECIAL PLACE

My special place is in my imagination
There are candy and sugar streams
There are chocolate rivers and candy cane umbrellas
There are gingerbread houses and candyfloss roofs
And chocolate rabbits
And the rain is Maltesers
And windows are toffee and that's my world.
It's a miracle.

Stephanie Taylor (9)
St Peter's CE Primary School, Bury

CANDY LAND!

The bright red lollipops!
The rain tastes of chocolate drops!
The sun of golden cream!
It tastes a little bit of Cadbury's Dream!
My favourite was the flake!
It helped me not to wake!
I paced further on!
I am now the only one!
It's getting too late!
I just can't wait!
I've woken now!
But now I will bow!
To Candy Land!
Rests in my hand!

Melissa Porter (9)
St Peter's CE Primary School, Bury

CATS

I have a cat, she's black and white
Her name is Molly
String hangs down
Her claws attach
When I'm in bed she lies next to me
That's my cat, Molly

I have a cat called Frisk
He always licks
He plays with your hair
And moves your hand, he will grab it
Even when you're asleep
That's my cat, Frisk.

Rachael Jones (10)
St Peter's CE Primary School, Bury

MY BEST FRIEND

My best friend, oh my best friend
Who is she?
Who is she?
She has dark brown hair and
She has green eyes
Who is she?
Who is she?
She wears glasses for the
Computer for
Reading, writing, TV
And the blackboard
Who is she?
Who is she?
She is Grace Nicholson
My best friend!

Kayleigh McDougall (9)
St Peter's CE Primary School, Bury

BLACKPOOL

B   is for Blackpool, an amusing place.
L   is for lights, shining brightly.
A   is for arcades.
C   is for cold beaches at night.
K   is for kicking a football on the beach.
P   is for pool tables in arcades.
O   is for the ocean, deep and wide.
O   is for oysters in the sea.
L   is for lovely views.

Jay Thornley (10)
St Peter's CE Primary School, Bury

You're Not Going Out

You're not going out!
Not looking like that!
You look like something
Brought in by the cat.
People will laugh at you,
Neighbours will stare at you.
That outfit, those colours
And that hair . . .
You are not going out,
When you look such a mess!
After all that I said
About sensible dress!
I'll disown you! I promise
I'm telling you flat:
You're not going out, Dad,
Not looking like that!

Matthew Bell (8)
St Peter's CE Primary School, Bury

In My Dream

As my dark and deep dream starts,
The sun has gone, the moon has shone,
A chocolate world all around,
My big chocolate bar I've found,
Take a bite and hear a sound,
The sun has risen in chocolate land,
As I wake in my bed,
I have chocolate on my head.

Colette Dickinson (9)
St Peter's CE Primary School, Bury

SEASONS

Winter is great when
Snow is falling on the ground
Oh how I wish it was snowing here

Spring is lovely with
Flowers on the ground all over
Hills and grass, roses, pansies, daisies all day

Summer is my favourite season
The sky is a clear blue
Not a cloud in sight, flowers and the sun

Autumn, when all the trees
Are bare, with the leaves on the ground
Layer on layer until winter comes.

Sophie Mansell (8)
St Peter's CE Primary School, Bury

MY POEM OF SUNSET

The sun goes up, the moon goes down,
The sea goes out, people might drown.

The sun goes down, the moon goes up,
People pouring a drink in a cup.

The sun goes up, the moon goes down,
People being mad and pulling a frown.

I see someone's winking eye,
Then I turn round and say goodbye.

Lauren Schofield (8)
St Peter's CE Primary School, Bury

MAN UNITED

M is for Manchester United who are the best
A is for Aston Villa who never score a goal
N is for no more goals for Liverpool

U is for USA who are losers
N is for night where teams play in the night
I is for injury when there's a bad tackle
T is for the tie when it's two-all
E is for energy for when they're running
D is for dirty tackle on Man United

S is for score when Owen scores a goal
C is for a cracking goal
O is for 'Oh!' when Man U miss a shot
R is for running all around the pitch
E is for an excellent goal

A is for accidental own goal

G is for goalkeeper
O is for Olé Gunnar Solskjaer
A is for Adidas football boots
L is for a lovely goal.

Jordan Bolton (8)
St Peter's CE Primary School, Bury

MY HOLIDAY

You took me on a lovely holiday to Italy and France
And on our holiday in Maratea we saw some Italians dance.
You took me on a great holiday to France and Italy,
It would be a lot more boring if we go to Sicily.

Connor Stansfield (9)
St Peter's CE Primary School, Bury

PERSIANS

P   is for Persians that are a cute type of feline
E   is for their eyes that are wide and glow in the dark
R   is for Rocky, the name of my blue Persian
S   is for silly that they sometimes are
I   is for an igloo which would be too cold for them
A   is for adventurous because some of them wander about a lot
N   is for nibbling food which some of them do
S   is for sweet which all of them are!

Emma Beckett (8)
St Peter's CE Primary School, Bury

MY HAMSTER

H   is for small, furry hamsters with cheek pouches
A   is for all the food they eat and hide
M   is for the monkey nuts that hamsters nibble at
S   is for storing all their food and eating some of it too
T   is for hamsters that never tidy up
E   is for all the food they eat and keep some of it in their pouches
R   is for all the running they do in their wheel and ball.

Louise Cunliffe (9)
St Peter's CE Primary School, Bury

FRIENDS

I have a friend, she is *great!*
For school she is late!
Always in bed, cuddled up with her ted,
I have a friend, she wants some money to spend.
She would rather hop than going to the shop.

I have a friend with a big, big bobble.
She likes the team Man U, so not Liverpool.
I could not have a better friend in my life.
My sister looks like a little mouse and I live in the same house.
My friend is not like that because she bought me a summer hat,
that's that!

Leanne Nabb (8)
St Peter's CE Primary School, Bury

JUGGLE TIME

Juggle, juggle, 1, 2, 3, hit up high
And catch the fly.
Juggle, juggle, 1, 2, 3, hit down below
And don't be too slow.
Juggle, juggle, out to the side
And reach out high.
Juggle, juggle, goodbye
See you soon, 1, 2, 3.

Amy Cowgill (9)
St Peter's CE Primary School, Bury

OCEAN

The ocean is bright then the sun is setting
The dolphins sing a lovely tune
Then the sound is soft, I can feel that ocean breeze
And when you go down to the sand
The weather is clear as the heavens above
You can feel the sun shine and the wind rushing through your hair
You can feel as you are in a practically perfect dream.

Christopher Walsh (9)
St Peter's CE Primary School, Bury

DAYTIME

It's light, I can hear birds singing, it's very early
The sun is nearly
Up in the sky shining high and bright
After being hidden all night
By a thick, black swoop
That makes flowers sleep and droop

Yum! Yum!
It's lunchtime and I've got loads of
Food in my tum
I'm not going to complain
But all the same
The weather's very dull
And I'm feeling rather full
That soup was very thick
And I think I'm going to be sick

Hi, I'm eating again
Munching, crunching, it all tastes the same
Tea is yum
But I prefer coffee in my tum
Oh wow, it's snowing
Soft and cold
Strong and bold
Frosty palace, crystal clear
Coming near
Snow angels flying
Parents sighing
Children laughing and playing
And saying,
'Frosty, snowy, winter day!'
As angels jump and dance and play.

Danielle Marshall (9)
St Peter's CE Primary School, Bury

PEBBLES

P   is for pom-poms we make.
E   is for excitement we have at birthdays.
B   is for buns we eat.
B   is for butterflies that don't live for long.
L   is for lily pads frogs leap from.
E   is for Eskimos that live at the North Pole.
S   is for sweetness that is around us.

Heather Mugglestone (8)
St Peter's CE Primary School, Bury

SWEETS

S   is for sweets that are delicious and tasty.
W   is for white chocolate that is creamy.
E   is for éclairs that are sucky and sweet.
E   is for gummy elephants that are sour.
T   is for Terry's chocolate orange.
S   is for sour snakes.

Jessica Fothergill (9)
St Peter's CE Primary School, Bury

THE JUNGLE

I was walking through the jungle and heard a rumble
I was walking down the path and saw a baby giraffe
Next mile on, I saw something going on
A pride of lions sleeping in the sun
The crocodiles lurking in the water
The snakes hiding in their shelter
Next to the snakes, there were some apes
Who were choking on some grapes.

Samantha Jade Timmins (10)
Sacred Heart RC Primary School

NETBALL

In netball I scored three
But in any other game that usually
Isn't me.
I ran and ran as fast as I could
The net is in sight, that's got to be good.
The ball is mine!
As we get ready to shout
Our joyful and encouraging line
Which means we have no doubt,
'Go Bianca! Go Bianca!'
I hear out loud
All this attention
Oh I feel so proud,
'The ball is in.'
My friends scream and shout
I wonder if these goals could mount?
The game has ended
I'm glad I attended.
So here's a reminder
For all you weak pups
You can give it to us hard
But us minty girls
Never give up!

Bianca Smith (11)
Sacred Heart RC Primary School

THE WOMAN WHO LIVED IN BIG BEN

There was a woman who lived in Big Ben
She couldn't count to ten
Her name was Grace
She fell on her face
And nobody saw her again.

She had a cousin who lived in Japan
Her dad was a robotic man
He had no heart
He was very smart
But he couldn't operate a chip pan.

Scott Holland (11)
Sacred Heart RC Primary School

POEM

I'm sat here thinking
into my chair I'm sinking.
Trying to make words rhyme,
it's taking me a long time.

I could write about a mouse
or I could put about my house.
No, that would be boring,
it would make people start snoring.

It's making my head hurt,
I've spilt pop on my skirt.
Everything's going wrong,
it would be easier to write a song.

Writing a poem is hard,
I might have to write it on card.
I'm getting rather mad
and I'm feeling very sad.

I'm not feeling well,
I'll need to get a bell.
I'm going to give up,
I've just been sick in my cup.

Sophie Flynn (11)
Sacred Heart RC Primary School

FOODS WE EAT

Food can be horrible,
Food can be mean,
They have disgusting habits
And are never clean!

Take peas for example
They jump on your plate.
They make little marks
And keep changing place.

And those hot dogs
Slip out of your hands,
They land on the floor
Then get stood on ten times.

There's only one thing I like for tea
That's the tasty cake
Whenever I come to eat it
I find it is a fake.

Holly Simmonds (10)
Sacred Heart RC Primary School

THE DEADLY FREE KICK

Alan Shearer taps the ball
Robert hits it through the wall
Solano goes up for a head
The crowd are silent, as if they are dead.

The Newcastle end go up with a cheer
Shearer finishes the match with a beer
He's man of the match, isn't that great
He's better than Solskaer. the player I hate.

Callum Maines (10)
Sacred Heart RC Primary School

SLEEPY WONDERWORLD

Turn off the lights,
Draw the curtains,
Prepare yourself for your sleep
Wonderworld.
A place, your very own,
Mine, you will hear
Is a hyper atmosphere
With . . .
Clowns a-hooting
Boots a-booting.
Legs a-legging it
Animals racing through my mind,
All this and more, you will find,
In your sleeping Wonderworld,
In your mind.

Alex Maxwell (8)
Sacred Heart RC Primary School

GOAL

He's running down the field
I think he's going for a goal,
He hits it -
There's silence in the stand
It's in!
The crowd are going wild
The players are jumping up and down
They've started play again
The whistle's gone,
They've won!

Martin Iddon (10)
Sacred Heart RC Primary School

STARS

The stars at night
They twinkle bright
They lead the way
For all to see
Without the stars
We'd lose our way.

The stars at night
They twinkle bright
Whilst the moon
Sails way up high
He has a smile for all to see
But especially just for you
and me.

Chantelle Johnson (10)
Sacred Heart RC Primary School

MY DOG JACK

My dog Jack
Likes to roll on his back.
He runs around like
A silly clown.
He likes to bat his ball to you
And beg for food too.
When he goes to bed
He lays his head
On his little ted.
He falls asleep
By counting sheep.

Rochelle Fairhurst (10)
Sacred Heart RC Primary School

ON THE WAY TO LINCOLNSHIRE

On the way to Lincolnshire
I write this poem
As we are getting near.

It was my birthday yesterday,
I got lots of pressies,
We're on our way.

On our way to the Travel Inn hotel
We're edging closer,
Hope it's not Hell.

We're going to a baptism
Of Bethan Maria Vaughn.

Niall McShane (11)
Sacred Heart RC Primary School

ROBOT

I am a robot
And I know a lot,
And I come from Africa
I can cook, I can clean
And I am rather mean.

I am very keen
And won't be seen.
You can switch me off,
And I won't really cough,
But I'm not very tough.

Sebastian Joe Kerridge (10)
Sacred Heart RC Primary School

MY GUINEA PIG

My guinea pig
Does a silly jig,
Sometimes in the night
When something gives her a fright.
It might be a cat
Or maybe a bat,
She soon settles down
When we stroke her little crown.
She's black and white
And never bites.

In the morning
When everyone's yawning,
My mum wakes in a rage
Because I won't clean Cynthia's cage.
Finally I clean her out
So my mum won't shout.
I give her fresh water and hay
Then she starts to play,
She runs about the house
Like a little mouse.
She hides behind Mum
She was having some fun,
She scurried around
Not making a sound.
My mum picked her up
To put her in the hutch,
Then at the end of the day
She snuggled in her hay.

Ashley Birchall (10)
Sacred Heart RC Primary School

FOOTBALL

Football, football, what a goal!
Football, football, what a goal!
Hit them soft or blast it off
Move, move to the football groove!
Pass it long or short. Shoot, shoot!
Football, football, what a goal!
Football, football, what a goal!
Take a throw-in or free kick, score!
Move, move to the football groove!

Darrell Jones (11)
Sacred Heart RC Primary School

THE EARLY MORNING BLUES

At 8 o'clock I jump out of my bed
I splash my face to clear my head.
Put on my uniform
Put on my shoes,
This is called the early morning blues!

Richard Lepori
Sacred Heart RC Primary School

THE MAGNIFICENT ELEPHANT

My elephant is big like a bus,
His trunk is like a big hosepipe.
His tail is like a fly swatter
His ears are like giant fans.
He resembles a big, black cloud,
I will wash my elephant with a jet wash.

Robert Spindlow (8)
The Heys Primary School

THE POWER OF MOONA

In the mystic world of magic
The old woman Moona dwells
Inside her glittery, golden tent
She sits beside her crystal ball
And predicts all to follow.

Moona's magic flows along
Yet no one knows it's there.
Her strangest transformations
From ugly to great beauty,
Her golden, flowing hair.

Moona is immortal
Her magic will go on.
Her strange and great desire
To palm read and know all . . .
The power of Moona's there.

Lauren Dowell (10)
The Heys Primary School

MY LITTLE BROTHER

My little brother always cries
He wants his bottle all the time
I'm his brother
Large and cool
But I'm on my way to school.

I rush home as fast as I can
To try and stop him crying
It makes me sad
And a little bit mad
To see him crying so.

I dress him in his trackie suit
Supporter of City is he
I'm glad to be
His brother you see
He makes me laugh when he has his tea.

Darrel Hinde (11)
The Heys Primary School

NIGHT

Night is a purring cat
Prowling around the world.
Revealing her polished stars,
She gleams gracefully.

When dawn crawls up
She peacefully lays her head.
Preparing for her long sleep,
Before she rises again.

The clearless sky begins to moan,
Wanting the gracious night
To strut her good looks
And make everyone sleep in peace.

So in the end
She is awoken,
She rises to the challenge.
Her beautiful, velvety blackness
In the jet-black sky.
Farewell my friend, farewell.

Lisa Mistry (11)
The Heys Primary School

My Special Sister

I make my way out of school
It's three fifteen on the dot,
My sister's picking me up tonight
I hope she's not late, like last night.
It's pretty frightening on my own, you know
When all the other kids and teachers
Have gone home!

I know she doesn't mean to be late,
But she just gets chatting with her mate.
Just a minute! Is this her I see?
Running down the street, she's waving at me.
The bus is coming, we can't be late
We must be home before half-past eight.

As the bus gets near home
Mum rings my sister's phone,
She's checking to see if we're okay
Because we're on our own.

Holly Taylor (10)
The Heys Primary School

Sports

I like footy and Man U
I like them and you will too
I'll hypnotise you
So you will too!

I like basketball and Philadelphia too
To score baskets, they jump higher than you
Philadelphia are cool and mint
The boys that play, run as fast as the wind.

I like cricket
I like hitting the wickets
I'm good with a bat
But not with a cat!

Andrew Atherton (10)
The Heys Primary School

AUTUMN

It's a time when the leaves turn gold and brown
And the trees turn their smiles to a frown.
In every year will come this time,
When the church bells start to chime.
So every animal gather your food, because autumn has arrived.

When the squirrels gather their nuts
And when the badgers go into their huts.
When the grass is jewelled and the trees are now bare,
Autumn has come and will go nowhere.
So every animal gather your food, because autumn has arrived.

In the night, so sparkling bright,
Where you shall a twinkling light.
Nothing else but you shall see,
No important thing only another bare tree.
No every animal has gathered its food, because now winter has arrived.

In autumn all this happens and nothing much more,
Hibernating is for animals and that's whom it's for,
Every animal is hibernating so now you can go to sleep
And close your bedroom door.

Zohaib Masood (11)
The Heys Primary School

ANIMALS OF THE WORLD

A lligators *snapppp!*
N ewts live in water
I guanas shed their skin
M onkeys swing from tree to tree
A nacondas are dangerous
L ambs make warm wool
S piders catch their prey in their webs.

O strich lay large eggs
F ish . . . only the perch is the true fish.

T oads croak
H orses gallop in their paddocks
E lephants have long trunks.

W hales are one of the largest mammals
O ctopus have eight legs
R hinos have horns
L lamas come from the camel family
D ogs . . . now that's my favourite animal!

Ryan Lee Gould (10)
The Heys Primary School

OWL

The owl comes out at night
Flying near the moon's light.
Looking for little mice,
Getting ready to pounce.

Trying to feed its babies,
Looking at the river with its sparkling eyes.
Flapping its soft, white feathers,
Sitting in the hollow
Of the old oak tree.

Looking at small stars
Glittering in the night sky,
Waiting for its loved one,
To pass by.

Shelby Gregson (11)
The Heys Primary School

LOVE IS ...

Love is beautiful
Love is frightening
Love is friendship
Love is hurting
Love is carefree
Love is worrying
Love is everything
Love is everything.

Chelsea Horrocks (10)
The Heys Primary School

MY SHADOW

My shadow is an enormous giant
It runs around doing what I do
When I go to bed, it comes with me
And then in the morning, it copies me too
Out in the sunshine waiting to play
My shadow and me, together all day.

Jade Lee (10)
The Heys Primary School

FAST FOOD

Running, running
Through the green, green forest
Roaring for dinner
I'm hungry!
Catch me my dinner!
I run on
Through the green, green forest
Tracking my dinner.

My claws catch a zebra
Mmm - stripy dinner!
My jaws and teeth
Will rip you apart.
My furry tummy will hide you
From the others.

Ready for supper?
You have no idea!
Deer!

Thomas Streeter (10)
The Heys Primary School

NIGHT

Night is when the golden cheese moon
Awakes from its morning sleep,
It shimmers on the silver street lamps.

Night is vicious and dark,
Stars begin to peep.
Birds and beasts and flowers
Soon will be asleep.

Yet of the dark, I have no fear,
But feel as safe as when it's light,
For I know God is with me here
And he will guard me through the night.

Amit Patel (10)
The Heys Primary School

FOG

Fog is the breath of a wolf,
Howling in the midnight sky,
It creeps around the universe
Saying, 'I am the best.'

Grey and cold,
Floating gracefully
As it slides across the sky,
Disturbing no one,
But sometimes it likes to scare
And cause chaos.
That is fog.

Amanda Hallsworth (11)
The Heys Primary School

THE MAGNIFICENT KANGAROO

My kangaroo is shiny like a diamond
His fists are like boxing gloves
His feet are like giant springs
His tail is like a snake
He resembles a bouncing rabbit
I will let him drink from my diamond river.

Tom Pugh (8)
The Heys Primary School

THE EAGLE

The eagle is the king of the sky
As it flies up high
You will hear its cry
Shooting by the wind.

Its wings as soft as a flower's petal
But its courage is as strong as metal,
Its claws like knives
That could take lives
As it swiftly swoops to the ground.

Its cunning eyes see everything
Underneath its chestnut wing
Its beak all gold
Can grip and hold
The littlest creature of all.

Nicholas Lee (11)
The Heys Primary School

THUNDER

Thunder is a vicious, reaching claw,
That pokes through the darkness,
The bright light perks up the town
And the sound shatters the windows,
The thunder comes
From the vaporous clouds
Above,
Thunder is a vicious, reaching
Claw.

Jason Motee (10)
The Heys Primary School

THE CROWD

The crowd sits silently
Waiting for the kick,
Nail-biting
You could even hear a pin drop.
The ball is placed down,
On the edge of their seats
The crowd starts chanting, 'England, England, England!'
It raises people's hopes
Everyone stands still,
He's gonna take the kick
The gasp goes round the stadium.
The kick goes wide
The crowd goes silent once again.

David Hibbert (10)
The Heys Primary School

BIKING

Fingers grip
Toes curl
Head down
Wheels whirl

Hair streams
Fields race
Ears sting
Winds chase

Breathe deep
Troubles gone
Just feel
Windsong.

Ferdaus Syed (11)
The Heys Primary School

THE MAGNIFICENT LION

My lion is speedy, like a cheetah,
His fur is a blanket laying on my bed,
His mane is a beautiful brown rug,
His teeth are diamonds, sparkling in his mouth
He resembles a huge, cuddly pussy cat.
He will eat fresh meat so he is big and strong.

Russell Nolan (9)
The Heys Primary School

THE MAGNIFICENT SHARK

The great white shark is the shadow of the water.
The bloody one of the sea.
The grey one that travels alone in the deep.
It is the rock of the rock pool.
The guard of the sea.
He lives in the deep of the ocean.

Ashley Minchin (8)
The Heys Primary School

MY CAT, TIGGER

My cat Tigger, so soft and cuddly,
When she is sleeping, you hear her purr.
She licks your face,
It feels like sandpaper.
Tigger likes to play with my sister,
She really loves her you know!

The meat she eats, she eats so slow,
She loves to drink water and milk.
She loves to eat chicken and fish,
When she smells them, she's right there.
Tigger the kitten,
I love her to bits.

Rebecca Johnson (10)
The Heys Primary School

IT WAS A NIGHTMARE BEST FORGOTTEN

Rat-a-tat-tat
The deafening sound of the machine gun fire,
I wish the time of healing was here,
The tanks blowing up the world,
Soldiers swarming out of the trenches,
On to no-man's-land,
To be killed.

Gary Stones (10)
Walmsley CE Primary School

BONFIRE NIGHT

On Bonfire Night I can feel heat as I look into the blazing fire.
The fireworks screech as they soar into the night sky.
When they explode the colours look like the rainbow.
The candyfloss melts as it fizzles in my mouth.
The air fills with excitement.
As the last firework blasts into the sky
It sets off dazzling colours.

Ben Collinson (8)
Walmsley CE Primary School

THE FOG OF WAR

The fog of war still hung over the battlefield,
In a few moments we would spring into action,
Swarming over no-man's-land,
There it was, I could see those brutal guns and
To think that there could be one bullet with my name on,
Sickened me with terror and grief.
I felt dissolved and lifeless,
But it was too late now to turn back,
My wife and children haunted me at that moment.
I leapt over the beaten trench,
But what I saw imprinted itself on my memory for as long as I lived,
It was a nightmare best forgotten.

Matthew Whittle (11)
Walmsley CE Primary School

LIFE IN THE TRENCHES

This war was a nightmare best forgotten,
But it was hard to.

I was on patrol in the trench, waiting for the enemy
To come over the desolate marshland.
Then suddenly, off the hillside, charged hundreds of men,
Maybe even thousands, with guns at the ready.
We climbed out of the trench and stood side by side,
Like a huge, armoured centipede,
Our heads and hearts were held high with hope.
The Germans fired.

Catherine Macdonald (11)
Walmsley CE Primary School

WORLD AT WAR!

Down, down, down in a deep, dark hole,
In a trench.
Sheltering from the exploding shower of bullets,
I hide away, like mouse from cat.
No food, no water, nothing.
Sitting on the cold, wet, muddy floor
Dying, yes, dying.
My leg covered in mud and blood,
Blown apart by those bombs.
The pain is too much to bear.
Up above, one gun could take a life,
Down here is where you'd die.
The pain . . .

Heather Whittaker (10)
Walmsley CE Primary School

LIFE IN THE TRENCHES

At the age of 17,
Boys marched to war,
Huddled together, shaking and whimpering,
Men running, screaming with horror,
Men being mown down, like ripe corn,
When the time had done its healing,
Heads and hearts were held up high,
With hope and expectation,
It was like the world was ending, just beside them,
It was a nightmare come true!

Kirsty Entwistle (11)
Walmsley CE Primary School

DOWN IN THE TRENCHES

Down in the trenches, cold, miserable,
No one to care.
Bombs raining around us,
Days without food.

Down in the trenches, mud walls all around us,
Praying for no attack.
Explosions lighting up the sky,
A nightmare best forgotten.

Down in the trenches, feeling sick with terror,
Chills shiver up my spine.
Hypnotised by the *rat-a-tat-tat* of guns,
Unfair to be alive.

Down in the trenches, cold, miserable.
Down in the trenches, no one to care.

Sara McCluskey (11)
Walmsley CE Primary School

SUMMER

Flowers in August are pink and blue,
Some are damp, with the dew.
The scent of daffodils, bright and yellow,
Sounds of birds, like a cello.
The sun shines down as bright as a daisy.
In summer ducklings hatch and swim down the Nile.
Tulips as red as a rose,
Bluebells ring like bells.
The last flower is a buttercup,
Now the flower is drying up.

Naomi Standish (10)
Walmsley CE Primary School

THE DINOCRUMP

Along the valley of the Ump,
Gallops the ferocious Dinocrump.
He is so very tall,
He thinks you are so very small.
He eats lots of meat,
Everyone says he has smelly feet.
His teeth are so very sharp,
They're even stronger than a shark.
For dessert he has mince pie,
Which makes him tell a wicked lie.
If you walk past his cave,
He will always give a friendly wave.
He is quite chubby
And he has a great buddy.
Oh how the creature stamps and roars,
Along the Ump's resounding shores.

George Matthew Bottomley (8)
Walmsley CE Primary School

I WANT TO PAINT . . .

I want to paint the sound of rippling waves,
I want to paint the smell of pizza,
I want to paint the taste of chocolate,
I want to paint the feel of a football,
I want to paint the sound of chirping birds,
I want to paint the smell of lasagne,
I want to paint the taste of fresh bread,
I want to paint the feel of a book cover,
I want to paint the sound of the wind,
But what do you want to paint?

Ben Dearden (9)
Walmsley CE Primary School

THE HIPPOCRUMP

Along the valley of the Ump
Gallops the fearful Hippocrump.
Although the Hippocrump is very brave,
Every time you see him he'll give you a wave.
He has a red belly
Made out of lots of jelly.
For his tea, he'll eat jam,
For his breakfast, he'll eat ham.
Last week he went on a ferry,
Now he's eating berries.
His teeth are sharp as nails,
He's playing on his PlayStation, but he fails.
As his mum comes in his room,
He'll look up in the sky and see the moon.
Downstairs on the couch he will lie,
As he gets disturbed by a fly.
His dad is very plump,
Where he works is a dump.
On the top of his hairy head,
Grows a patch of dazzling red.
The Hippocrump lives on a hill,
Though today, the Hippocrump is ill.
At seven-thirty he'll take a nap,
While his dad looks at the map.
The Hippocrump is a United fan,
Yesterday he was eating jam.
The jam grows beside the yellow lake,
His thousands of teeth began to ache.
Oh how the creature stamps and roars,
Along the Ump's resounding shores.

Harry Smith (10)
Walmsley CE Primary School

A RUMBLE IN THE JUNGLE

I went into the jungle
and I heard a big rumble.
I saw a lion roar
and a squirrel on the floor.
I was scared, really scared
but I had done it for a dare.
I went further in
and it was quite dim.
I saw a faint tree,
then I realised there were three.
One had feathers,
one was called Heather
and the other was all alone,
its wish was just to go home.
The wind suddenly blew,
I sneezed and went, *atishoo!*
The trees started to rumble
and I heard my tummy grumble
I looked down at my pocket clock
and I saw it was 5 o'clock.
I ran as fast as I could,
Mum will be in the kitchen. Yeah! Sure she would.
She asked me about my day, I told her about the tree,
then Sally, my cousin came in, she's only three.
Mum said, 'Silly you,'
then asked, 'but are you sure it's true?'

Amy Beaven (8)
Walmsley CE Primary School

SPELL FOR A PERFECT CHRISTMAS

Into the cauldron you must throw . . .

Shiny baubles on the tree,
Spiky holly, nice and green,
Snow that comes down from the sky,
A nice warm mince pie.
going shopping for Christmas clothes,
Rudolph's big red nose,
All the big Santa sights,
The three men following the star,
A big brown chocolate bar.
A big party packed with fun,
A beautiful angel on top of the tree
And lots of presents just for me.
Christmas pies that people bring,
Christmas carols that children sing,
Santa Claus who I admire,
Jazzy stockings by the fire.

Santa, Santa, make reindeer fly,
Make all the magic go into the sky.

Abbi Knowles (9)
Walmsley CE Primary School

IN THE TRENCHES

It was a nightmare, an endless one,
The guns spat shells from their fiery mouths,
That was the familiar fearful sound of the machine gun,
The sound of terror,
A bullet might have my name on,
The number of bullets could only be described as a swarm of locust.

Nicholas Fletcher (11)
Walmsley CE Primary School

The Hippocrump

Along the valley of the Ump,
Gallops the fearful Hippocrump.
If you're walking down the path,
Make sure he's had a bath.
He has three humps on his back
And he has ten birds for a snack.
He has golden hair
And he hates eating a pear.
He has a great big belly
And it's like green jelly.
His eyes are sparkly and green,
If he gives you a grin, you'll not be seen.
His favourite food is chocolate bars
And he hates looking at the stars.
His tail is like a snake
And his fingers are like a rake.
Oh how the creature stamps and roars
Along the Ump's resounding shores.

Abigail Nelson (8)
Walmsley CE Primary School

In The Trenches

I am a ghost in the trenches
Watching and listening to the war go on
As I walk on, watching and listening
Watching and listening to my loved ones die
Hundreds fall as I watch and listen
Deafening guns go *bang, bang, bang . . .*
I am a ghost in the trenches
Watching and listening to the war go on.

Sophie Hughes (10)
Walmsley CE Primary School

In The Bottom Of The Ocean

In the bottom of the ocean, I can see
Beautiful blue dolphins
Swimming in a miraculous pattern.

In the bottom of the ocean, I can see
Lots of mermaids dancing round a heart-shaped diamond,
Almost like the heart of the ocean.

In the bottom of the ocean, I can see
A humungous shipwreck, with skeletons,
About the size of you and me.

In the bottom of the ocean, I can see
Thousands of little fishes swimming
In and out of rocks.

In the bottom of the ocean, I can see
Sharks swimming round five jellyfish
And that scares me.

I like to see all of these things in the sea.
It's something special,
Why don't you go and see?

Harriet Winstanley (9)
Walmsley CE Primary School

What's Red?

Red is the colour of my sister when I pinch her diary.
Red is the colour of the fiery red sun.
Red is the colour of the never-forgotten poppy.
Red is the colour of the wilting rose.
Red is the colour of gory blood dripping from a cut.
Red is the colour of the sizzling fire.

Red is the colour of my dripping paint.
Red is the colour of my Valentine gift.
Red is the colour of the fizzy Coca-Cola can.
Red is the colour of a sparkler on Bonfire Night.
Red is the colour of a disco light.
What do you think red is?

Ben Bailey (9)
Walmsley CE Primary School

THE HIPPOCRUMP

Along the valley of the Ump,
Gallops the feared Hippocrump.
If you're walking down a path,
Hope he's just had a bath.
He has a great big belly
And it shakes just like a jelly.
His eyes are sparkly and green,
If he winks you will never be seen.
His grin is really very wide,
So avoid walking by his side.
He has a bump on his back,
And eats nine monkeys for a snack.
His favourite food is human bars,
So his teeth shine like stars.

Down in the deep purple lake
Swims the Hippocrump after a snake.
Oh how he got a fright
When it turned to bite.
Oh how the creature stamps and roars
Along the Ump's resounding shores.

Eleanor Worrall (9)
Walmsley CE Primary School

I WANT TO . . .

I want to go to the planet Mars,
I want to drive two sports cars,
I want to zoom off in a rocket,
I want to shut my door and lock it.
I want to have a treat,
I want to eat some sweets,
I want to fly on a magic mat,
I want to wear a red hat.
I want to read a book,
I want to have a look,
I want to sail a boat,
I want to wear my woolly coat.
I want to study some English,
I want to make my feet feel all ticklish.

Bethany Thornborough (10)
Walmsley CE Primary School

THE HIPPOCRUMP

Along the valley of the Ump
Gallops the fearful Hippocrump.
He crawls along the slippery floor
And bangs hard into the door.
His eyes are bright sparkling blue,
But he doesn't even have a clue.
His teeth are perfect, glistening white,
His golden hair is very bright.
When he wants something to eat
He has lots and lots of meat.
Oh how this creature stamps and roars
Along the Ump's resounding shores.

Victoria Moss (9)
Walmsley CE Primary School

MY ALIEN

My alien has red blood as his desire
And on his head burns hot fire.
He lives on Mars
And will only eat Mars bars.
He uses a rocket to travel around,
But needs to practise on landing on the ground.
He sometimes travels around the bounty
Because he's in the alien county.
On his bed,
Lies someone dead.
All his friends drive hover-bikes
And on his arms he has ten spikes.
He always has a big shave,
Plus he's always brave.

Ben Sudworth (8)
Walmsley CE Primary School

MY TOYS IN THE NIGHT

When everybody has gone to sleep,
My toys come out to play.
They creep out of my room and say,
'We will go downstairs.'
They have ice cream and watch TV
And they all have a laugh.
Some of the teddy bears sing
And some dress up,
One dolly wears a hat.
While the dog jumped on the cat,
Then they saw the sun and crept back upstairs.

Amelia Lohan (9)
Walmsley CE Primary School

MY DOGS

My dog Rob will sleep all day,
My dog Skip always wants to play,
My dog Dan is always hungry for food,
My dog George is always getting in a mood,
My dog Amy is always very posh,
My dog Holly never wants a wash,
My dog Laura is always very loud,
My dog Katie will not make a sound,
My dog Camilla loves to play with a ball,
My dog Josh will never come, even if you call,
My dog Ben always will bark,
My dog Harriet likes to go for walks in the dark,
My dog Sam's favourite colour is red.
My favourite one? Must be all of them!

Sophie Arnold (9)
Walmsley CE Primary School

IN THE TRENCHES

Dying men lie wounded in the filthy trenches,
Morbid thoughts swirl in their minds,
The monotonous screech of the shells,
Reverberates through their ears.
Sick with terror,
As horrendous screaming rings out for all to hear.
Foreboding dinginess of the musty air,
Hanging over enemy lines.
A lone grenade explodes, the sound of warning.
Bullets whipping and whining past them,
Drawing ever closer,
To the sanctuary of the trenches.

Thomas Howard (10)
Walmsley CE Primary School

FOOD

I never eat at the table,
I try and try but am never able.
My favourite food is sausage and chips,
Although my dad prefers Doritos and dips.
I like chicken nuggets too,
But my dad says they're not good for you.
I love ice cream,
But I am only allowed it if my fingers are clean.
My grandad loves fish,
But I only eat it if it's out of a dish.
I love it when my mum says, 'Dinner's ready.'
I rush to the table and my mum says, 'Hey, steady.'
Even though I'm the only one,
I am glad when it has all gone.

Katie Shaw (9)
Walmsley CE Primary School

DOLPHINS

Dolphins are blue, dolphins are grey,
Sometimes you see them every day.
If you're at the beach in a boat,
You may see their smooth, shimmering coat.
They skim the waves with a splash!
When they see you, they swim off with a dash.
Their eyes are beady and black,
Their mouths close with a *clack.*
Dolphins swoop and zoom out of waves,
Normally you see them on sunny days.
Dolphins, dolphins, pure and blue,
I like dolphins, do you?

Mary Hargreaves (9)
Walmsley CE Primary School

PLAY TIME

At play time we all run round
Making such an awful sound.
The boys are playing with a ball,
But then it goes over the wall!
In the corner there is a girl
And she is eating a yummy Twirl.
I have Skittles for my snack,
While I'm eating them, someone hits me on the back!
I see someone climbing up a tree,
But it isn't me!
I can hear a shouting noise,
I bet it's those mean boys.
You can have such a good game of tig,
Because the playground is so big!

Laura Brady (9)
Walmsley CE Primary School

WHAT IS RED?

Red is the colour of my dad's face when I'm naughty,
Red is the colour of the sunset,
Red is the colour of people's hair,
Red is the colour of blood,
Red is the colour of war and hate,
Red is the colour of a disco light,
Red is the colour of blazing fire,
Red is the colour of brick and stone,
Red is the colour of an apple,
Red is the colour of a tin of paint,
Red is a glorious colour.

Sam Hawkins (9)
Walmsley CE Primary School

LIFE IN THE TRENCHES

Life in the trenches a long time ago,
All to think about is my dear wife Margot.

Thinking of her miles away at home,
Thinking of Margot all alone.

Down in the trenches,
Everywhere you look, lots of muddy fences.

The battle cry rang,
We marched out and sang.

God save our soul,
Please God, save our souls!

Harriet Coxon (11)
Walmsley CE Primary School

THEY HAVE . . .

They have a tanker
And a ship with an anchor.
They have ferries
Made out of cherries.
They have a man called Terry
And he lives in Bury.
They have a castle
And the king is a bit of a hassle.
They have a spaceship
The size of a pip!

Ben Ellis (9)
Walmsley CE Primary School

I WANT TO PAINT MY LIFE IN A TRENCH

I want to paint the courage it took to fight,
I want to paint the smell of the wet, soggy mud,
I want to paint the sound of the *rat-a-tat-tat* of the gunshot,
I want to paint the sight of a plane flying across the sun,
Shooting at my trench,
Dropping down their weapons,
I want to paint the gloom of the outer world,
As the bombs drop.

Danielle Dutton (11)
Walmsley CE Primary School

THE TERRIBLE TRENCHES

It was horrendous. The *rat-a-tat-tat* of guns!
My men being slaughtered in front of me!
We stormed out, rifles held high!
People being shot as the night was nigh!
Bullets whipped and whined past my head!
The terrible trenches I called them!
Then, so soon, my captain was shot dead!
Blood splattered everywhere, I felt like dying!

Robert Feakin (10)
Walmsley CE Primary School

I WANT TO PAINT . . .

I want to paint the taste of sweets,
I want to paint the look of treats,
I want to paint the feel of snow,
I want to paint a flickering glow,

I want to paint the feel of joy,
I want to paint a cheeky boy,
I want to paint all sorts of things,
But what do you want to paint?

Sam Hulme (8)
Walmsley CE Primary School

WHAT IS?

What is water sparkling in the sun?
What is the sun burning in space?
What is space flooding the galaxy?
What is grass on the football pitch?
What is a football pitch as big as a park?
What is a park defended by children?
What is a school full of technology?
What is fascinating about technology?

Alastair MacDonald (8)
Walmsley CE Primary School

THE ALIEN

The alien comes from Mars,
He eats delicious chocolate bars.
His name is Zack,
He has an extra gigantic back.
He always trips,
Every day he eats a portion of chips.
His body is really fat,
He has a little pet rat.

Joshua Lowe (9)
Walmsley CE Primary School

In The Trenches

In the trenches it is dark and gloomy,
In the trenches a seventeen-year-old boy stands,
In the trenches he remembers,
He broke his ankle,
He is scared sick,
He was in agony,
He is trying to save people in the darkness,
Hoping he can get out of the war,
But he knows his bullet will find him.

John Whipp (11)
Walmsley CE Primary School

In The Trenches

In the trenches life was hell,
Just awful, like a prison cell.
Always watching, never sleep,
Staying within the trenches' keep.
Curled in a ball, hands on our heads,
Not comfy, no beds.
Every day, always scared
And when we looked, the Germans glared.

Samantha Coop (11)
Walmsley CE Primary School

I Want To Paint . . .

The sound of birds singing,
The taste of treacle,
The smell of pizza,
The feeling of happiness,

The sound of waves rippling,
The taste of chocolate,
The smell of strawberries,
The smell of Sunday lunch.

Ian Ranson (8)
Walmsley CE Primary School

LIFE IN THE TRENCHES

Bang! Another day at war,
The *rat-a-tat-tat* of the machine guns,
The trenches were a nightmare best forgotten,
The soldiers filled with courage,
Heads and hearts high with expectation,
Bullets whipping and whining,
The early morning sun, spoilt with our fighting,
Losing friends, a very gruesome sight!

Sophie Anderson (10)
Walmsley CE Primary School

THE FROG

A long-leaper,
A fly   catcher,
A water-breather,
A fast attacker,
A quick swimmer,
A wide-eyed starer,
A tadpole-layer,
A lily-lover.

John Phillips (10)
Westhoughton Parochial CE Primary School

LIGHTNING

A jagged dagger,
A thunder lover,
A tree breaker,
A murderous killer,
A flicker in the sky,
But a night waker to my eye.

David Parkinson (11)
Westhoughton Parochial CE Primary School

THE SUN

An orange, bouncy ball,
In the exquisite, big, blue sky,
Hates the moon,
So very high,
A day-gazer
Which falls to sleep at night.

Chloe Snape (10)
Westhoughton Parochial CE Primary School

SMOKE!

A grey cloud,
A human poisoner,
An alarm starter,
A silent murderer,
A house intruder.

Melissa Aspinall (10)
Westhoughton Parochial CE Primary School

ALARM CLOCK

A dream deafener,
A loud beeper,
A number changer,
A time keeper.

A noisy waker,
A sleep surprise,
A number thinker,
A time to rise.

A dream breaker
A day starter,
A morning maker,
An eye opener.

Gina Barker (11)
Westhoughton Parochial CE Primary School

THE FANTASTIC FOOTBALL BOOTS

Goal scorer,
Shot misser,
Cross maker,
Dirty fouler,
Penalty taker,
Hard kicker,
Help saver,
Big booter,
Great attacker,
Cup helper,
Cup winner.

Matthew Brooking (10)
Withnell Fold Primary School

I FOUND A LANTERN

I found a lantern under the stairs
And wondered what it was doing there.
Was it old or was it new?
I really do not have a clue!
Does it save lives,
Or does it cause death?
Will the candle flicker,
Or will it burn bright?
Is the glass cracked,
Or is it all right?
Did someone own it,
Or was it just there?
Was it used for pleasure,
Or maybe for work?
It might be an antique,
Or maybe even modern.
Did an adult own it,
Or did it protect a child?
It lies there silently
And does not answer,
That's the life of that lantern
That lives under our stairs.

Rachael Critchley (10)
Withnell Fold Primary School

MR BROWN

I have a teddy called Mr Brown
And he never wears a frown

He comforts me when I am down
He comes with me into town

He helps me tidy my bedroom
He is my best friend I presume

He is always there for me
He looks after me when I hurt my knee

He always helps me when I'm stuck
Or when I am reading a book

That is Mr Brown, my very own ted
Now it is time to go to bed.

Nikki Evans (10)
Withnell Fold Primary School

THE FOOTY BOOT

Dirty, old, filthy, footy boot
The mud hides your colours
Red, white and black.

Did you ever kick the ball,
Or maybe score a goal?
Have your studs worn away,
Or torn up your sole?

Did you score a hat-trick,
Did you get a foul?
And when you won the World Cup,
Did the crowd shout out loud?

Were you a professional's boot?
Did you belong to a boy?
Hung up in the cupboard,
A neglected footy boot.

I wish you could tell me your secrets,
Old footy boot.

Tom Smith (10)
Withnell Fold Primary School

THE BOTTLE

That water bottle is there every day
and I want it to go.
I don't like the bottle cos it's round
and if it gets dropped on the floor.
My mum would get mad
and she would be cross.
So I would love it to go.
So something else can take its place.
But not another bottle,
Mum, not another bottle.
How about a small plant
or something along that line?
So how about that, Mum?
It might be a bit more fun.

Luke Davy (10)
Withnell Fold Primary School

THE FOOTBALL BOOT

The old, neglected football boot,
Hanging at the back of the wardrobe.
Did you score the winning World Cup goal,
Or did you belong to the best ever defender?
Did you score from a goal kick,
Or were you just used in training?
Did you belong to a professional player,
Or just a boy in his school team?
The boot just hung there silently,
Leaving me to wonder.

Joseph Tohill (10)
Withnell Fold Primary School

MY SHELLS

Shells come from sea to shore
Hundreds, thousands, maybe more
My shell is called a pelican's foot
I found it on a Corfu beach
It's half starfish and half crab shell
It's quite spiky and twirly too
It's curly, swirly, with sharp spikes
It's bumpy on the outside
But smooth on the inside
It's many shades of purple and blue
Mixed with creamy-yellowy white
In some places it's shiny and bright
It's pink and glittery inside
It has jagged patterns all over itself
It's a beautiful shell, I wish I had more.

Maria Peck (10)
Withnell Fold Primary School

SEASHELLS ON THE SHORE

Seashells on the shore
They will be spiky and bright,
They will be pretty and light
Colourful and very shiny.

Smooth and rough, round and square
Hard and striped like a tiger,
Smelly seaweed from the sea
In the deep ocean blue.

Sarah Ashton (10)
Withnell Fold Primary School

MY TEDDY

Look! My teddy's over there,
He is sitting by the chair
With a ribbon round his neck,
He is better than anything hi-tech!

He is mine and he is all hairy,
He never makes me feel very scary.
He lives with me on my bed,
The good thing about him, he doesn't need to be fed.

I'm very emotional, that's the bad thing,
He makes me better when I feel bad,
I love my ted, he's the best,
He is better than all the rest.

I've had my teddy for a very long time,
My teddy always puts me right,
It's me who is usually *wrong*.
I'm going to keep *him* forever.

Heather Charnley (10)
Withnell Fold Primary School

TEDDY

Cuddly, furry, that's my ted,
Sweet, adorable, sitting on my bed.
When his big brown eyes look at me,
I know our friendship was meant to be!

When I am away from home,
He comforts me and keeps me calm,
By putting his warm fur close to me,
To make me happy!

I love him with all my heart
And he's had that ribbon from the very start.
All in all, I love him so
And I take him everywhere I go.

Charlotte Jackson (11)
Withnell Fold Primary School

THE LANTERN BURNING

You lift up the latch and swing it to the right,
Then put the candle in and let it burn bright.
Some could be scented and others not,
Do not touch it because it's very hot!

It should flicker through the night,
Then it might jump up and bite.
Gold and bronze it might glow,
One, two, three, come on blow!

You can use it anywhere,
Even while walking up the stair.
Why do you use it in the light,
When we need it in the night?

Was it used for work or play
And why don't the colours stay?
Orange, yellow, gold or red,
I blew it out and now it's dead.

And where have the colours gone?
I loved it when it shone.
Now it's time to shut your eyes tight,
When it shone it was a beautiful sight.

Tara Miller (11)
Withnell Fold Primary School

My Golden Boots

Goal scorer
Shot striker
Dirty fouler
Great tackler
Running, sprinting
Jumping, jogging
Limping, hopping
Golden boots
Hat-trick hero
Penalty taker
Great cross
Great goal
My golden boots.

Jos White (11)
Withnell Fold Primary School

Lantern

The lantern light is bright
It is a beautiful sight.
It also has a handle
And a scented candle.
Undo the catch
And strike the match.
Light the candle,
Then pick up the handle.
Your mum tucks you into bed,
Then it might glow gold or red.

Josie McVittie (10)
Withnell Fold Primary School

MY TEDDY

My teddy is raggy and old
Because of me it will never be sold
It is a wonderful colour of brown
And it never wears a frown.

It comforts me when I cry
Or whenever I tell a lie
My teddy is very furry
And he's also extremely hairy.

His big, brown eyes look straight at me
And I know we were meant to be.

Bryony Gorton (9)
Withnell Fold Primary School

TEDDY

Cuddly, warm and human-like,
I'll never leave him alone.
I tell him all my worries.

When I go to bed at night
I never need to say
Goodnight.

When I wake up in the morning
He is always there waiting,
Smiling for me happily.

Megan Radziminski (9)
Withnell Fold Primary School

THAT'S MY TED!

Cuddly, soft, that's my ted,
He comforts me when I cry,
He sleeps with me in bed.
When I'm worried,
He makes me happy,
I can tell him all my secrets,
Cos I know he'll never tell or say a thing,
In fact, I can tell him everything.

Brown and fluffy, that's my ted,
I've had him since I was young,
He goes everywhere with me,
When I go to sleepovers, he comes too.
Even on Christmas morning
He comes downstairs with me.
I love my ted, he's the best,
He's better than all the rest.

Jessica Parker (11)
Withnell Fold Primary School